미국교과서 리스닝 with DICTATION

Level 2

오석태 지음

길벗스쿨

저자 오석태

한국 외국어대학교에서 한국어와 영어를 전공하고, 학생들의 영어 실력 향상을 위해 자신만의 영어 노하우를 개발하며 강의를 했다. 1988년 KBS FM Radio를 통해 방송계에 입문하면서 TV와 라디오에서 활동하는 방송영어 스타로 자리매김했으며, 2008년부터 영어 콘텐츠 개발 전문 저자로 활동하며 ELC Contents라는 출판사 겸 콘텐츠 개발 전문회사를 설립하였다. 현재 ELC Contents의 영어교재 출판 상표(imprint)인 OST English를 통해 책을 출간하고 있다.

저서 〈미드가 들리는 리스닝 트레이닝〉, 〈영어는 입으로〉, 〈영어 회화의 결정적 표현들〉, 〈오석태의 영어회화 끝장 레슨〉, 〈악마는 프라다를 입는다 자막없이 보기〉, 〈영어회화 끝장패턴〉, 〈오석태의 말하는 영어〉, 〈영어회화 무작정 따라하기〉, 〈미국교과서 READING〉 등

⏐ 일러두기

〈미국교과서 리스닝 with DICTATION〉은 2013년 출간된 〈기적의 미국교과서 받아쓰기〉의 개정판입니다.

미국교과서 리스닝 with DICTATION Level 2
American Textbook Listening with DICTATION Level 2

초판 발행 · 2020년 9월 30일

지은이 · 오석태
발행인 · 이종원
발행처 · 길벗스쿨
출판사 등록일 · 2006년 7월 1일 | **주소** · 서울시 마포구 월드컵로 10길 56 (서교동)
대표 전화 · 02)332-0931 | **팩스** · 02)323-0586
홈페이지 · www.gilbutschool.co.kr | **이메일** · gilbut@gilbut.co.kr

기획 및 책임 편집 · 이경희, 김미경(moon@gilbut.co.kr) | **디자인** · 박찬진, 윤미주 | **제작** · 이진혁
영업마케팅 · 김진성, 박선경 | **웹마케팅** · 박달님, 권은나 | **영업관리** · 정경화 | **독자지원** · 송혜란, 홍혜진

전산편집 · 윤미주 | **본문삽화** · 배성환, 양지원, 김태균, 박기종
인쇄 · 벽호 | **제본** · 벽호 | **녹음** · YR 미디어

ISBN 979-11-6406-262-1 64740 (길벗 도서번호 30490)
     979-11-6406-260-7 64740 (세트)
정가 13,000원

독자의 1초를 아껴주는 정성 길벗출판사
길벗 | IT실용서, IT/일반 수험서, IT전문서, 경제실용서, 취미실용서, 건강실용서, 자녀교육서
더퀘스트 | 인문교양서, 비즈니스서
길벗이지톡 | 어학단행본, 어학수험서
길벗스쿨 | 국어학습서, 수학학습서, 유아학습서, 어학학습서, 어린이교양서, 교과서

길벗스쿨 공식 카페 〈기적의 공부방〉 · cafe.naver.com/gilbutschool
인스타그램 / 카카오플러스친구 · @gilbutschool

제 품 명 : 미국교과서 리스닝
     with DICTATION Level 2
제조사명 : 길벗스쿨
제조국명 : 대한민국
전화번호 : 02-332-0931
주   소 : 서울시 마포구 월드컵로
     10길 56 (서교동)
제조년월 : 판면에 별도 표기
사용연령 : **11세 이상**
KC마크는 이 제품이 공통안전기준에
적합하였음을 의미합니다.

머리말

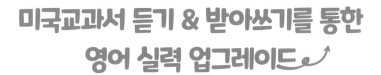
미국교과서 듣기 & 받아쓰기를 통한
영어 실력 업그레이드

미국교과서는 영어 보물창고

미국 초등학교 교과서로 영어를 공부하는 학생들이 늘어나면서 이제 미국교과서는 영어 리딩을 위한 필수 과정이 된 것 같습니다. 과학, 사회, 예체능 과목의 지문을 읽으며 교과 지식과 영어를 동시에 공부하는 것은 선생님과 학생들에게 좋은 영어 학습인 것은 분명합니다. 하지만 미국교과서를 리딩으로만 배우기에는 한계가 있습니다.

영어 공부에 왕도는 없지만, 정도는 있습니다. 바르고 좋은 문장을 많이 외우는 것입니다. 문장을 외우는 가장 좋은 방법은 반복적으로 듣고, 따라 말하고, 받아쓰는 것입니다. 미국교과서는 좋은 문장으로 가득 찬 보물창고로, 가장 정확하고 세련된 현대적인 영어 표현을 배울 수 있습니다. 이를 외우고 활용한다면 학생들은 자신만의 영어 보물창고를 갖게 될 것입니다.

단계적으로 접근하는 듣고, 받아쓰기

이 교재의 최종 학습 목표는 과목별로 한 단락에서 두 단락 분량의 교과서 지문을 통으로 외우는 것입니다. 교과서 지문을 외우는 과정이 지겹고 고통스럽지 않도록 여섯 단계로 구성되어 있습니다. 먼저 단어와 문장을 따라 말하는 연습을 합니다. 다음에는 단어와 문장을 듣고 받아쓰는 연습을 합니다. 이 과정을 거치면 기본 단어와 문장을 저절로 암기하게 됩니다. 다음 단계는 앞에서 배운 단어와 문장이 반복적으로 나타나는 짧은 문장과 대화문을 듣고 받아쓰는 훈련을 합니다. 마지막으로 지금까지 배운 모든 표현이 들어가 있는 교과서 지문을 듣고 받아씁니다. 마지막 단계를 마치게 되면 학습자는 교과서 지문을 통으로 외우는 수준이 될 것입니다.

교과서를 듣고, 받아쓰는 과정에서 영어 듣기는 물론 머릿속에 입력된 영어 문장들은 자연스럽게 쓰기와 말하기에도 도움이 될 것입니다.

이 책으로 학생들이 좋은 영어 문장을 맛보고 알아가는 즐거움을 느끼고, 이를 통해 영어 공부에 자신감을 얻을 수 있기를 바랍니다.

오석태

이 책의 구성 및 학습법

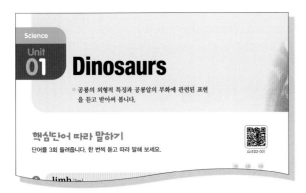

주제 확인

듣고 받아쓸 교과 과목 및 지문의 주제를 확인합니다. 공부하기 전에 주제에 대해서 한 번 생각해 보고 학습에 들어가면 학습 효과도 높고 학습한 내용도 오래 기억할 수 있습니다.

핵심단어 따라 말하기

받아쓸 주제와 관련된 핵심단어 10개를 듣고 따라 말해 봅니다. 각 단어를 3회씩 들려줍니다. 원어민의 음성을 듣고 따라 말하면서 단어의 정확한 발음과 의미를 익혀 보세요.

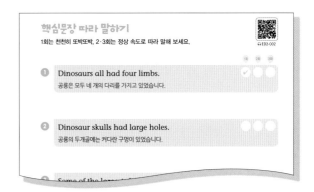

핵심문장 따라 말하기

받아쓸 교과 지문의 주요 내용이 포함된 핵심문장 4개를 듣고 따라 말해 봅니다. 각 문장을 느린 속도와 정상 속도로 3회 들려줍니다. 연음과 억양에 주의하면서 원어민의 음성을 듣고 따라 말해 보세요.

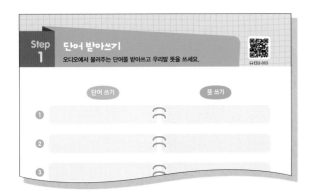

단어 받아쓰기

〈핵심단어 따라 말하기〉에서 연습한 10개 단어를 듣고 받아쓰는 단계입니다. 원어민이 불러주는 영어 단어를 듣고 영어 단어와 그 의미를 써 보세요.

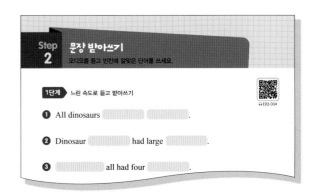

문장 받아쓰기

〈핵심문장 따라 말하기〉에서 연습한 4개의 문장을 듣고 받아쓰는 단계입니다. 1단계에서는 천천히 읽어주는 문장을 듣고 문장 속 단어 1~2개를 받아쓰고, 2단계에서는 정상 속도로 읽어주는 문장을 듣고 문장 속 단어 2~4개를 쓰면 됩니다.

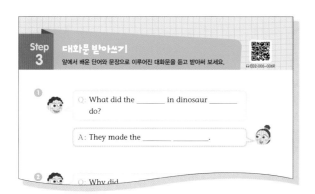

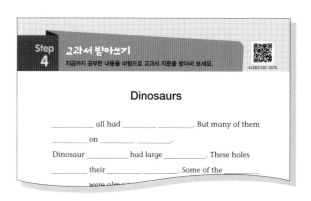

대화문 받아쓰기

배운 단어와 문장을 이용해서 두 사람이 대화를 나눕니다. 받아쓸 때는 받아쓰기용 MP3 파일을 이용하고, 잘 받아 적었는지 확인하거나 다시 듣고 싶을 때는 파일명에 R자가 붙은 복습용 MP3 파일을 이용하면 됩니다.

교과서 받아쓰기

오늘 배운 주제와 관련된 교과서 지문이 제시됩니다. 앞 단계에서 배운 단어, 문장이 빈칸으로 되어 있습니다. 잘 듣고 빈칸을 채우면서 교과서 지문을 완성합니다. 받아쓸 때는 받아쓰기용 MP3 파일을 이용하고, 잘 받아 적었는지 확인하거나 다시 듣고 싶을 때는 파일명에 R자가 붙은 복습용 MP3 파일을 이용하면 됩니다.

정답 및 해석

본문 문제들의 정답 및 스크립트, 대화문과 지문에 대한 우리말 해석을 수록하였습니다. 정답 및 해석이 되지 않는 문장들의 의미를 확인하면서 다시 한번 생각하고 점검해 볼 수 있습니다.

QR코드

스마트폰의 QR코드 인식기능을 활용하여 해당 음원을 쉽게 들을 수 있습니다. 또한 홈페이지(www.gilbutschool.co.kr)에서도 MP3 파일을 무료로 다운받으실 수 있습니다.

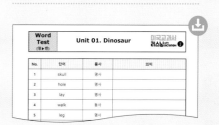

온라인 부가자료

Word List, Word Test, Key Sentence Writing 등 다양한 부가 학습자료를 홈페이지(www.gilbutschool.co.kr)에서 무료로 다운받으실 수 있습니다.

Music

Arts

Unit 01 Dinosaurs

＊공룡의 외형적 특징과 공룡알의 부화에 관련된 표현을 듣고 받아써 봅니다.

핵심단어 따라 말하기

단어를 3회 들려줍니다. 한 번씩 듣고 따라 말해 보세요.

🎧 ED2-001

			1회	2회	3회
❶	**limb** [lim]	명 팔다리, 다리	✔	◯	◯
❷	**skull** [skʌl]	명 두개골, 해골	◯	◯	◯
❸	**hatch** [hætʃ]	동 부화하다, 알에서 나오다	◯	◯	◯
❹	**hole** [houl]	명 구멍	◯	◯	◯
❺	**nest** [nest]	명 둥지	◯	◯	◯
❻	**dinosaur** [dáinəsɔ̀ːr]	명 공룡	◯	◯	◯
❼	**lay** [lei]	동 알을 낳다	◯	◯	◯
❽	**walk** [wɔːk]	동 걷다	◯	◯	◯
❾	**leg** [leg]	명 다리	◯	◯	◯
❿	**develop** [divéləp]	동 성장하다, 발달하다	◯	◯	◯

핵심문장 따라 말하기

1회는 천천히 또박또박, 2·3회는 정상 속도로 따라 말해 보세요.

ED2-002

1회   2회   3회

1 **Dinosaurs all had four limbs.**

공룡은 모두 네 개의 다리를 가지고 있었습니다.

2 **Dinosaur skulls had large holes.**

공룡의 두개골에는 커다란 구멍이 있었습니다.

3 **Some of the largest skulls were almost as long as a car.**

가장 큰 두개골 중 몇몇은 거의 자동차만큼 길었습니다.

• as + 원급 + as : ~만큼 …한

4 **All dinosaurs laid eggs.**

모든 공룡은 알을 낳았습니다.

단어 쓰기   뜻 쓰기

1

2

3

4

5

6

7

8

9

10

Step 2 문장 받아쓰기

오디오를 듣고 빈칸에 알맞은 단어를 쓰세요.

1단계 느린 속도로 듣고 받아쓰기

🎧 ED2-004

❶ All dinosaurs _____ _____ .

❷ Dinosaur _____ had large _____ .

❸ _____ all had four _____ .

❹ Some of the largest _____ were almost as _____ as a _____ .

2단계 정상 속도로 듣고 받아쓰기

🎧 ED2-005

❶ Some of the _____ _____ were almost _____ _____ as a _____ .

❷ _____ dinosaurs _____ _____ .

❸ _____ all had _____ _____ .

❹ Dinosaur _____ had _____ _____ .

1

Q: What did the _____ in dinosaur _____ do?

A: They made the _____ _____.

2

Q: Why did _____ need _____?

A: Because they _____ _____ in nests.

3

Q: How many _____ did dinosaurs _____?

A: They had _____ _____.

4

Q: What happened to the _____ dinosaurs until they were _____ to _____?

A: They _____ in their _____.

Dinosaurs

_____ all had _____ _____. But many of them _____ on _____ _____.

Dinosaur _____ had large _____. These holes _____ their _____ _____. Some of the _____ _____ were almost as _____ as a _____.

All dinosaurs _____ _____–some in _____ just like _____ do today. The _____ _____ in the _____ until it was _____ to _____.

Science

* 과학의 정의 및 분류, 그리고 과학자들의 업적과 관련된
표현을 듣고 받아써 봅니다.

핵심단어 따라 말하기

단어를 3회 들려줍니다. 한 번씩 듣고 따라 말해 보세요.

🎧 ED2-008

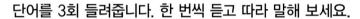

| | | 1회 | 2회 | 3회 |

① **universe** [júːnəvə̀ːrs] 　　명 우주 　　✓ ○ ○

② **truth** [truːθ] 　　명 진실, 사실 　　○ ○ ○

③ **mystery** [místəri] 　　명 미스터리 　　○ ○ ○

④ **search** [səːrtʃ] 　　명 탐구, 조사 　　○ ○ ○

⑤ **knowledge** [nálidʒ] 　　명 지식 　　○ ○ ○

⑥ **tiny** [táini] 　　형 아주 작은 　　○ ○ ○

⑦ **discover** [diskʌ́vər] 　　동 발견하다 　　○ ○ ○

⑧ **variety** [vəráiəti] 　　명 다양성 　　○ ○ ○

⑨ **understand** [ʌ̀ndərstǽnd] 　　동 이해하다 　　○ ○ ○

⑩ **material** [mətí(ː)əriəl] 　　명 재료, 물질 　　○ ○ ○

핵심문장 따라 말하기

1회는 천천히 또박또박, 2·3회는 정상 속도로 따라 말해 보세요.

🎧 ED2-009

1회 2회 3회

1 **Science is the search for truth and knowledge.**

과학은 진실과 지식에 대한 추구입니다.

• **search for** ~의 추구, 탐구

2 **It helps us understand life, the universe, and almost everything.**

그것은 우리가 생명과 우주, 그리고 거의 모든 것에 대해서 이해할 수 있도록 돕습니다.

• **help** + 목적어 + 동사원형/**to** 부정사: ~가 …하도록 돕다

3 **Scientists study a huge variety of things and discover new facts.**

과학자들은 매우 다양한 것들을 연구하며 새로운 사실을 발견합니다.

• **a variety of** 여러 가지의 ~, 다양한 ~

4 **Scientists also study the mysteries of space.**

과학자들은 또한 우주의 미스터리도 연구합니다.

단어 받아쓰기

오디오에서 불러주는 단어를 받아쓰고 우리말 뜻을 쓰세요.

🎧 ED2-010

단어 쓰기　　　　　　　　　　　뜻 쓰기

1

2

3

4

5

6

7

8

9

10

문장 받아쓰기

오디오를 듣고 빈칸에 알맞은 단어를 쓰세요.

1단계 느린 속도로 듣고 받아쓰기

ED2-011

❶ Scientists also study the _____ of _____.

❷ Science is the _____ for _____ and knowledge.

❸ _____ study a huge _____ of things and _____ new facts.

❹ It helps us _____ life, the _____, and almost everything.

2단계 정상 속도로 듣고 받아쓰기

ED2-012

❶ It _____ us _____ life, the _____, and almost everything.

❷ Science is the _____ for _____ and _____.

❸ Scientists also _____ the _____ of _____.

❹ _____ study a _____ _____ of things and _____ new _____.

1

Q: What is _____ the _____ for?

A: Science is the _____ for _____ and _____.

2

Q: What do _____ _____?

A: Scientists study a _____ _____ of things.

3

Q: What are _____?

A: _____ are the things that _____ _____ everything around us.

4

Q: What does _____ _____ us do?

A: Science helps us _____ life and the _____.

Science

_____ is the _____ for _____ and _____.
It helps us _____ _____, the _____, and
almost everything.

_____ study a huge _____ of things and
_____ new _____. They studied _____ and
_____ that atoms are the _____ _____ and
_____ up _____ around us. Scientists also
_____ the _____ of _____.
There is _____ science, _____ science, _____
and _____ science, _____ science, etc.

Advances in Science

* 과학의 발달과 사상가 아리스토텔레스가 현대 과학자들에게
끼친 영향에 관한 표현을 듣고 받아써 봅니다.

핵심단어 따라 말하기

단어를 3회 들려줍니다. 한 번씩 듣고 따라 말해 보세요.

🎧 ED2-015

			1회	2회	3회

❶ **invention** [invénʃən]   명 발명(품)   ✔ ○ ○

❷ **solve** [salv]   동 해결하다, 풀다   ○ ○ ○

❸ **discovery** [diskʌ́vəri]   명 발견   ○ ○ ○

❹ **recommend** [rèkəménd]   동 제안하다   ○ ○ ○

❺ **thinker** [θíŋkər]   명 사상가, 생각하는 사람   ○ ○ ○

❻ **influence** [ínfluəns]   동 영향을 주다   ○ ○ ○

❼ **experiment** [ikspérəmənt]   명 실험   ○ ○ ○

❽ **begin** [bigín]   동 시작하다   ○ ○ ○

❾ **pose** [pouz]   동 제기하다   ○ ○ ○

❿ **history** [hístəri]   명 역사   ○ ○ ○

핵심문장 따라 말하기

1회는 천천히 또박또박, 2·3회는 정상 속도로 따라 말해 보세요.

🎧 ED2-016

1회   2회   3회

❶ Science begins with problems.

과학은 문제로부터 시작됩니다.

❷ They wanted to solve the problems that life posed.

그들은 인생이 제기한 문제를 해결하고 싶어 했습니다.

• **that:** ~가 …하는 것

❸ The scientists made many great inventions and discoveries.

그 과학자들은 수많은 위대한 발명과 발견을 이뤄냈습니다.

❹ Many scientists have been influenced by Aristotle.

많은 과학자들은 아리스토텔레스의 영향을 받았습니다.

• **have been + 과거분사 :** ~되어 왔다, ~받아 왔다

단어 쓰기

뜻 쓰기

1

2

3

4

5

6

7

8

9

10

ED2-018

1단계 느린 속도로 듣고 받아쓰기

1 Many _____ have been _____ by Aristotle.

2 Science _____ with _____ .

3 They wanted to _____ the _____ that life posed.

4 The scientists made many great _____ and _____ .

ED2-019

2단계 정상 속도로 듣고 받아쓰기

1 The _____ made many great _____ and _____ .

2 _____ _____ have been _____ by Aristotle.

3 They wanted to _____ the _____ that life _____ .

4 _____ _____ with _____ .

대화문 받아쓰기

앞에서 배운 단어와 문장으로 이루어진 대화문을 듣고 받아써 보세요.

ED2-020~020R

1

Q: What did Aristotle _____?

A: He recommended that people _____ out _____ to test their _____.

2

Q: How did we get great _____ and _____?

A: The _____ _____ them.

3

Q: What were the _____ _____ like?

A: They were _____ _____.

4

Q: What did _____ _____ to do?

A: They wanted to _____ the problems that _____ _____.

Advances in Science

Science _____ with _____.

The great _____ were all _____. They wanted

to _____ the _____ that _____ _____.

The scientists made many _____ _____ and

_____, which have _____ the _____ of

_____.

More than 2,000 _____ _____, the Greek _____

Aristotle _____ that people look at _____ and

_____ out _____ to _____ their _____.

Many _____ have been _____ by Aristotle.

Leonardo da Vinci and Galileo Galilei

* 레오나르도 다빈치와 갈릴레오 갈릴레이의 다양한 분야에 걸친
업적과 관련된 표현을 듣고 받아써 봅니다.

핵심단어 따라 말하기

단어를 3회 들려줍니다. 한 번씩 듣고 따라 말해 보세요.

🎧 ED2-022

		1회	2회	3회

1 **inventor** [invéntər]　　명 발명가　✔ ◯ ◯

2 **painter** [péintər]　　명 화가　◯ ◯ ◯

3 **telescope** [téləskòup]　　명 망원경　◯ ◯ ◯

4 **prove** [pru:v]　　동 증명하다　◯ ◯ ◯

5 **parachute** [pǽrəʃùːt]　　명 낙하산　◯ ◯ ◯

6 **instrument** [ínstrəmənt]　　명 악기　◯ ◯ ◯

7 **astronomer** [əstránəmər]　　명 천문학자　◯ ◯ ◯

8 **plan** [plæn]　　명 도면, 설계도, 계획　◯ ◯ ◯

9 **technology** [teknálədʒi]　　명 기술　◯ ◯ ◯

10 **unfortunately** [ʌnfɔ́ːrtʃənitli]　　부 불행하게도　◯ ◯ ◯

핵심문장 따라 말하기

1회는 천천히 또박또박, 2·3회는 정상 속도로 따라 말해 보세요.

ED2-023

1회   2회   3회

1 Leonardo da Vinci was a painter, scientist, and inventor.

레오나르도 다빈치는 화가이자 과학자, 그리고 발명가였습니다.

2 He drew plans for helicopters, airplanes, and parachutes.

그는 헬리콥터, 비행기, 그리고 낙하산의 설계도를 그렸습니다.

3 Unfortunately, the technology of his time was not **good enough to** build any of them.

불행히도, 그가 살았던 당시의 기술은 그것들 중 어느 하나라도 만들어 낼 만큼 훌륭하지 않았습니다.

● 형용사+enough to : ~하기에 충분히 …한

4 Galileo Galilei was an astronomer and instrument maker.

갈릴레오 갈릴레이는 천문학자이자 악기제조자였습니다.

단어 쓰기

뜻 쓰기

1

2

3

4

5

6

7

8

9

10

문장 받아쓰기

오디오를 듣고 빈칸에 알맞은 단어를 쓰세요.

1단계 느린 속도로 듣고 받아쓰기

🎧 ED2-025

❶ Galileo Galilei was an _____ and _____ maker.

❷ Leonardo da Vinci was a painter, _____, and _____.

❸ He drew _____ for helicopters, airplanes, and _____.

❹ Unfortunately, the _____ of his time was not good _____ to build any of them.

2단계 정상 속도로 듣고 받아쓰기

🎧 ED2-026

❶ Leonardo da Vinci was a _____, _____, and _____.

❷ He _____ _____ for _____, airplanes, and _____.

❸ _____, the _____ of his time was not good _____ to _____ any of them.

❹ Galileo Galilei was an _____ and _____.

ED2-027~027R

① Q: What did Galileo Galilei _____ about the _____?

A: He _____ that the earth _____ around the _____.

② Q: How did Galileo Galilei prove the _____ about the _____?

A: He _____ at the _____ system through a _____.

③ Q: Did Leonardo da Vinci build the _____ that he _____?

A: No. The _____ of his time was not good _____ to _____ them.

④ Q: What did Leonardo da Vinci _____?

A: He drew _____ for _____, airplanes, and _____.

Leonardo da Vinci and Galileo Galilei

Leonardo da Vinci(1452-1519) was a _____, _____, and _____. He drew _____ for _____, _____, and _____. Unfortunately, the _____ of his time was not _____ _____ to _____ any of them.

Galileo Galilei(1564-1642) was an _____ and _____ _____. He _____ that the _____ moves around the _____ by _____ at the _____ system through a _____.

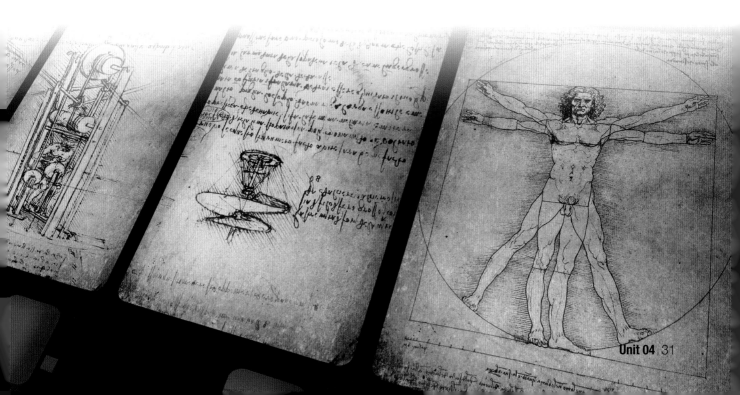

Isaac Newton and Thomas Edison

✳ 과학자 아이작 뉴턴과 발명가 토머스 에디슨의 생애에 관한 표현을 듣고 받아써 봅니다.

핵심단어 따라 말하기

단어를 3회 들려줍니다. 한 번씩 듣고 따라 말해 보세요.

🎧 ED2-029

		1회	2회	3회
① **mathematician** [mæ̀θəmətíʃən]	몡 수학자	✔	○	○
② **deaf** [def]	혱 귀가 들리지 않는	○	○	○
③ **physicist** [fízisist]	몡 물리학자	○	○	○
④ **suffer** [sʌ́fər]	동 고통 받다, 괴로워하다	○	○	○
⑤ **light bulb** [lait bʌlb]	몡 전구	○	○	○
⑥ **orbit** [ɔ́ːrbit]	몡 궤도	○	○	○
⑦ **gravity** [grǽvəti]	몡 중력	○	○	○
⑧ **force** [fɔːrs]	몡 힘	○	○	○
⑨ **realize** [rí(ː)əlàiz]	동 깨닫다	○	○	○
⑩ **planet** [plǽnit]	몡 행성	○	○	○

핵심문장 따라 말하기

1회는 천천히 또박또박, 2·3회는 정상 속도로 따라 말해 보세요.

🎧ED2-030

1회 2회 3회

① **Isaac Newton was a physicist and mathematician.**

아이작 뉴턴은 물리학자이자 수학자였습니다.

② **He studied forces and light.**

그는 힘과 빛에 대해 연구했습니다.

③ **Thomas Edison was an inventor.**

토머스 에디슨은 발명가였습니다.

④ **At 12, he suffered from scarlet fever and became deaf.**

12살 때, 그는 열병을 앓았고, 귀가 멀게 되었습니다.

• **suffer from** ~로 인해 고통 받다

단어 받아쓰기

오디오에서 불러주는 단어를 받아쓰고 우리말 뜻을 쓰세요.

🎧 ED2-031

단어 쓰기   뜻 쓰기

1

2

3

4

5

6

7

8

9

10

⌒ED2-032

1단계 느린 속도로 듣고 받아쓰기

1 Thomas Edison was an _____.

2 At 12, he _____ from scarlet fever and became _____.

3 Isaac Newton was a _____ and mathematician.

4 He studied _____ and light.

⌒ED2-033

2단계 정상 속도로 듣고 받아쓰기

1 He studied _____ and _____.

2 Isaac Newton was a _____ and _____.

3 Thomas _____ was an _____.

4 At 12, he _____ from scarlet _____ and _____ _____.

1

Q: _____ was Thomas _____?

A: He was an _____.

2

Q: _____ did Thomas Edison _____?

A: He _____ more than 1,000 things, including _____ _____ and _____.

3

Q: _____ was Isaac _____?

A: He was a _____ and a _____.

4

Q: What is _____?

A: Gravity is a _____ that keeps the _____ in _____ around the sun.

Isaac Newton and Thomas Edison

Isaac Newton(1643-1727) was a _____ and _____. He studied _____ and _____. He _____ there must be a _____ that keeps the _____ in _____ around the _____. Today, we _____ this force as _____.

Thomas Edison(1847-1931) was an _____. At 12, he _____ from scarlet _____ and became _____.

However, he made more than 1,000 _____, including long-lasting _____ _____ and _____.

Inventions

❋ 발명품의 정의와 그 예와 관련된 표현을 듣고 받아써 봅니다.

핵심단어 따라 말하기

단어를 3회 들려줍니다. 한 번씩 듣고 따라 말해 보세요.

🎧 ED2-036

		1회	2회	3회

❶ **idea** [aidí(:)ə] 　명 발상, 아이디어 ✓ ○ ○

❷ **wheel** [ʰwiːl] 　명 바퀴 ○ ○ ○

❸ **create** [kriéit] 　동 창조하다 ○ ○ ○

❹ **easier** [íːziər] 　형 더 쉬운, 더 수월한 ○ ○ ○

❺ **character** [kǽriktər] 　명 등장인물, 특성 ○ ○ ○

❻ **invention** [invénʃən] 　명 발명품 ○ ○ ○

❼ **writer** [ráitər] 　명 작가, 저자 ○ ○ ○

❽ **life** [laif] 　명 생활, 삶 ○ ○ ○

❾ **use** [juːz] 　동 사용하다 ○ ○ ○

❿ **magnetic compass** [mægnètik kʌ́mpəs] 　명 자기 나침반 ○ ○ ○

핵심문장 따라 말하기

1회는 천천히 또박또박, 2·3회는 정상 속도로 따라 말해 보세요.

🎧ED2-037

❶ New things that are made or created are called inventions.

만들어지거나 창조된 새로운 것을 발명품이라고 부릅니다.

- be called ~라고 불리다

❷ Ideas can also be called inventions.

발상도 또한 발명품으로 불릴 수 있습니다.

- can 〈조동사〉+ 동사원형 : ~할 수 있다

❸ Inventions have made life easier for us.

발명품은 우리를 위해서 삶을 더 수월하게 만들어 주었습니다.

- make + 목적어 + 목적보어 : ~을 …하게 하다, 만들다

❹ Paper was invented in China.

종이는 중국에서 발명되었습니다.

- be동사 + 과거분사 : ~되다

단어 받아쓰기

오디오에서 불러주는 단어를 받아쓰고 우리말 뜻을 쓰세요.

ED2-038

단어 쓰기

뜻 쓰기

1

2

3

4

5

6

7

8

9

10

1단계 느린 속도로 듣고 받아쓰기

🎧 ED2-039

1 [   ] was [   ] in China.

2 [   ] can also be [   ] inventions.

3 Inventions have made [   ] [   ] for us.

4 [   ] things that are made or [   ] are called inventions.

2단계 정상 속도로 듣고 받아쓰기

🎧 ED2-040

1 [   ] have made [   ] [   ] for us.

2 [   ] was [   ] in [   ].

3 [   ] can also be [   ] [   ].

4 [   ] that are made or [   ] are called [   ].

🎧 ED2-041~041R

1

Q: According to the _____, what was the _____ when it was first _____?

A: It was an _____ when it was _____ made.

2

Q: What can _____ _____?

A: Writers can invent _____ and then write _____ about them.

3

Q: What have the _____ and _____ done for people?

A: They have made _____ _____ for people.

4

Q: What do people call _____ things that are made or _____?

A: People _____ them _____.

Inventions

_____ things that are _____ or _____ are
called _____. The _____ and the _____
were _____ when they were _____ made.
_____ can also be called _____. _____ can
_____ _____ and then _____ stories about
them.
Inventions have made _____ _____ for us. The
_____ was first _____ in Mesopotamia. _____
was _____ in China.

Unit 07
South America

*※ 남아메리카의 면적과 안데스 산맥, 아마존 강에 관한 표현을 듣고 받아써 봅니다.

핵심단어 따라 말하기

단어를 3회 들려줍니다. 한 번씩 듣고 따라 말해 보세요.

🎧 ED2-043

			1회	2회	3회
❶	**run** [rʌn]	통 이어지다, 달리다	✔	○	○
❷	**spine** [spain]	명 척추, 등뼈	○	○	○
❸	**east** [iːst]	명 동쪽	○	○	○
❹	**west** [west]	명 서쪽	○	○	○
❺	**continent** [kántənənt]	명 대륙	○	○	○
❻	**flow** [flou]	통 흐르다	○	○	○
❼	**western** [wéstərn]	형 서쪽의	○	○	○
❽	**side** [said]	명 쪽, 측, 측면	○	○	○
❾	**south** [sauθ]	명 남쪽	○	○	○
❿	**north** [nɔːrθ]	명 북쪽	○	○	○

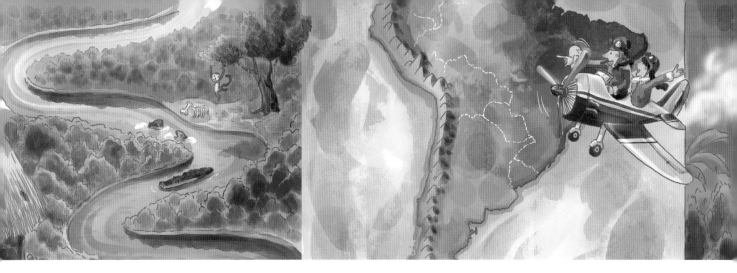

핵심문장 따라 말하기

1회는 천천히 또박또박, 2·3회는 정상 속도로 따라 말해 보세요.

ED2-044

1회   2회   3회

① **The fourth-largest continent is South America.**

네 번째로 큰 대륙은 남아메리카입니다.

② **The Andes Mountains on the western side of the continent are the longest chain of mountains in the world.**

그 대륙의 서쪽 면에 있는 안데스 산맥은 세계에서 가장 긴 산맥입니다.

● the + 최상급 + of + 복수명사 : ~ 중에서 가장 …한 것

③ **The Amazon River cuts the South American continent as it flows from west to east.**

아마존 강은 서쪽에서 동쪽으로 흐르면서 남아메리카 대륙을 나눕니다.

● as〈접속사〉 : ~하면서, ~함에 따라

④ **It is the second-longest river in the world after the Nile.**

그것은 나일 강 다음으로 세계에서 두 번째로 긴 강입니다.

● the + 최상급 + in + 장소 : ~에서 가장 …한 것

단어 받아쓰기

오디오에서 불러주는 단어를 받아쓰고 우리말 뜻을 쓰세요.

ED2-045

단어 쓰기　　　　　　　　　뜻 쓰기

1

2

3

4

5

6

7

8

9

10

문장 받아쓰기

오디오를 듣고 빈칸에 알맞은 단어를 쓰세요.

🎧 ED2-046

1단계 느린 속도로 듣고 받아쓰기

① The Andes Mountains on the _____ _____ of the continent are the _____ chain of mountains in the world.

② The fourth-largest _____ is South _____.

③ The Amazon _____ cuts the South American continent as it _____ from west to east.

④ It is the second-longest _____ in the _____ after the Nile.

🎧 ED2-047

2단계 정상 속도로 듣고 받아쓰기

① The _____ -largest _____ is _____ _____.

② It is the _____ -longest _____ in the _____ after the Nile.

③ The Amazon _____ _____ the South American continent as it _____ from _____ to east.

④ The Andes _____ on the _____ _____ of the _____ are the _____ chain of mountains in the world.

1

Q: In this _____, why does it say the Andes Mountains _____ like a _____?

A: Because they _____ from _____ to _____.

2

Q: How does the Amazon _____ _____ the South American _____?

A: It _____ from _____ to _____.

3

Q: _____ are the Andes _____?

A: The Andes Mountains are on the _____ of _____ _____.

4

Q: What is the _____ _____ in the world?

A: The _____ is the longest river in the _____.

South America

The fourth-largest _____ is _____ _____.

The _____ Mountains on the _____ _____ of

the _____ are the _____ chain of _____

in the world. They _____ from _____ to _____

like a _____.

The Amazon _____ _____ the _____ American

_____ as it _____ from _____ to _____.

It is the _____-longest river in the _____ after the

_____.

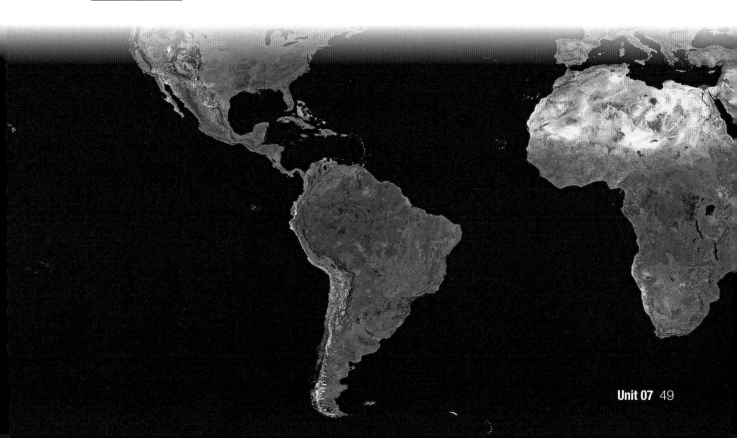

Unit 08 **Antarctica**

✴ 남극 대륙의 지리적 위치와 기후 등에 관한 표현을 듣고 받아써 봅니다.

핵심단어 따라 말하기

단어를 3회 들려줍니다. 한 번씩 듣고 따라 말해 보세요.

🎧 ED2-050

		1회	2회	3회
1 consider [kənsídər]	동 간주하다, 여기다	✔	○	○
2 cover [kʌ́vər]	동 덮다	○	○	○
3 thick [θik]	형 두꺼운	○	○	○
4 average [ǽvəridʒ]	명 평균 형 평균의	○	○	○
5 South Pole [sauθ poul]	명 남극	○	○	○
6 southernmost [sʌ́ðərnmòust]	형 최남단의	○	○	○
7 windy [wíndi]	형 바람이 부는	○	○	○
8 permanently [pə́ːrmənəntli]	부 영구적으로	○	○	○
9 desert [dézərt]	명 사막	○	○	○
10 research station [rísəːrtʃ stéiʃən]	명 연구소	○	○	○

핵심문장 따라 말하기

1회는 천천히 또박또박, 2·3회는 정상 속도로 따라 말해 보세요.

🎧 ED2-051

1회 2회 3회

1 **Antarctica is the earth's southernmost continent.** ✓ ◯ ◯

남극 대륙은 지구 최남단의 대륙입니다.

2 **About 98% of Antarctica is covered with ice.** ◯ ◯ ◯

남극의 약 98%는 얼음으로 뒤덮여 있습니다.

• be covered with ~로 뒤덮여 있다

3 **It is considered a desert.** ◯ ◯ ◯

그곳은 사막으로 간주됩니다.

• be considered ~로 간주되다

4 **No humans permanently live in Antarctica.** ◯ ◯ ◯

남극에서는 사람이 영구적으로 살 수 없습니다.

단어 받아쓰기

오디오에서 불러주는 단어를 받아쓰고 우리말 뜻을 쓰세요.

ED2-052

단어 쓰기　　　　　뜻 쓰기

1

2

3

4

5

6

7

8

9

10

ED2-053

1단계 느린 속도로 듣고 받아쓰기

1 About 98% of Antarctica is ＿＿＿＿＿ with ＿＿＿＿ .

2 ＿＿＿＿＿＿ is the earth's ＿＿＿＿＿＿ continent.

3 No ＿＿＿＿＿ permanently ＿＿＿＿＿ in Antarctica.

4 It is ＿＿＿＿＿ a ＿＿＿＿＿ .

ED2-054

2단계 정상 속도로 듣고 받아쓰기

1 No ＿＿＿＿ ＿＿＿＿＿ ＿＿＿＿＿ in Antarctica.

2 It is ＿＿＿＿＿ a ＿＿＿＿＿ .

3 About 98% of ＿＿＿＿＿ is ＿＿＿＿ with ＿＿＿＿ .

4 ＿＿＿＿＿＿ is the earth's ＿＿＿＿ ＿＿＿＿ .

1

Q: How _____ is _____?

A: It is the _____-largest _____.

2

Q: Can people _____ _____ in Antarctica?

A: _____. No _____ permanently _____ in _____.

3

Q: How _____ is the _____ in Antarctica?

A: It is at _____ 1.6 kilometers _____.

4

Q: Is Antarctica a _____?

A: Yes. It is _____ a _____.

Antarctica

_____ is the earth's _____ _____.

It is at the _____ _____ and is the fifth-largest

_____.

About 98% of Antarctica is _____ with _____. This

ice is at _____ 1.6 kilometers _____. Antarctica,

on _____, is the _____, _____, and

_____ continent. It is _____ a _____. No

_____ _____ live in Antarctica.

However, _____ live at _____ _____ in

Antarctica _____ the year.

Australia

✳ 호주의 특징에 관한 표현을 듣고 받아써 봅니다.

핵심단어 따라 말하기

단어를 3회 들려줍니다. 한 번씩 듣고 따라 말해 보세요.

🎧 ED2-057

	1회	2회	3회

❶ **partly** [pá:rtli]   부 부분적으로 ✔ ◯ ◯

❷ **except** [iksépt]   전 ~를 제외하고 ◯ ◯ ◯

❸ **contact** [kántækt]   명 접촉, 연락 ◯ ◯ ◯

❹ **contain** [kəntéin]   동 포함하다 ◯ ◯ ◯

❺ **develop** [divéləp]   동 성장하다, 발달하다 ◯ ◯ ◯

❻ **far** [fɑ:r]   부 멀리   형 먼 ◯ ◯ ◯

❼ **island** [áilənd]   명 섬, 제도 ◯ ◯ ◯

❽ **nation** [néiʃən]   명 국가, 나라 ◯ ◯ ◯

❾ **without** [wiðáut]   전 ~ 없이 ◯ ◯ ◯

❿ **part** [pɑ:rt]   명 지역, 부분 ◯ ◯ ◯

핵심문장 따라 말하기

1회는 천천히 또박또박, 2·3회는 정상 속도로 따라 말해 보세요.

🎧 ED2-058

① The smallest continent is the island of Australia in the South Pacific.

가장 작은 대륙은 남태평양에 있는 호주 섬입니다.

② It is the only continent **that** contains just one nation.

그곳은 단 하나의 국가만 포함하는 유일한 대륙입니다.

• that : ~하는 것

③ Partly because so much of it is desert, Australia has **the fewest people of all the continents** except Antarctica.

부분적으로는 호주 대부분의 지역이 사막이기 때문에, 호주는 남극 대륙을 제외한 모든 대륙 중에서 사람이 가장 적게 사는 지역입니다.

• the + 최상급 + of + 복수명사 : ~ 중에서 가장 …한 것

④ Because Australia is **far from** all of the other continents, its animals developed without contact with animals from other parts of the world.

호주는 다른 대륙으로부터 멀리 떨어져 있기 때문에, 그곳의 동물들은 세계 다른 지역에 있는 동물들과의 어떠한 접촉도 없이 자랐습니다.

• far from ~로부터 멀리 떨어져

단어 쓰기

뜻 쓰기

1

2

3

4

5

6

7

8

9

10

1단계 느린 속도로 듣고 받아쓰기

🎧 ED2-060

❶ It is the only _____ that _____ just one nation.

❷ The _____ continent is the island of _____
in the South Pacific.

❸ Partly because so much of it is _____, Australia has the
fewest people of all the _____ except _____.

❹ Because Australia is far from all of the other _____,
its animals _____ without contact with animals
from other _____ of the world.

2단계 정상 속도로 듣고 받아쓰기

🎧 ED2-061

❶ _____ because so much of it is _____, Australia has
the _____ people of all the _____ except _____.

❷ It is the _____ _____ that _____ just one _____.

❸ Because Australia is _____ from all of the other _____,
its animals _____ without _____ with animals
from other _____ of the world.

❹ The _____ _____ is the island of _____
in the South _____.

🎧 ED2-062~062R

1

Q: How many _____ are in _____?

A: Australia _____ just one _____.

2

Q: Are there a lot of _____ and _____ in Australia?

A: No. So _____ of Australia is _____.

3

Q: How have _____ in Australia _____?

A: They have _____ without _____ with animals from other _____.

4

Q: What is the _____ _____?

A: The smallest continent is the _____ of _____.

Australia

The _____ _____ is the _____ of _____ in the South _____. It is the _____ continent that _____ just one _____. _____ because so much of it is _____, Australia has the _____ people of all the _____ _____ Antarctica.

Because Australia is _____ from all of the other _____, its _____ _____ without _____ with animals from other _____ of the _____.

America's Past

※ 북미 대륙에 거주했던 원주민과, 콜럼버스의 아메리카 대륙
발견에 관한 표현을 듣고 받아써 봅니다.

핵심단어 따라 말하기

단어를 3회 들려줍니다. 한 번씩 듣고 따라 말해 보세요.

🎧 ED2-064

				1회	2회	3회

❶ **explorer** [iksplɔ́ːrər]   명 탐험가   ✔ ○ ○

❷ **however** [hauévər]   접 그러나, 하지만   ○ ○ ○

❸ **land** [lænd]   동 착륙하다, 도착하다   ○ ○ ○

❹ **sail** [seil]   동 항해하다   ○ ○ ○

❺ **early** [ə́ːrli]   형 초창기의 부 일찍   ○ ○ ○

❻ **native** [néitiv]   형 원주민의   ○ ○ ○

❼ **country** [kʌ́ntri]   명 나라, 국가   ○ ○ ○

❽ **later** [léitər]   부 나중에, 뒤에   ○ ○ ○

❾ **different** [dífərənt]   형 다른, 각각 다른   ○ ○ ○

❿ **continent** [kʌ́ntənənt]   명 대륙   ○ ○ ○

핵심문장 따라 말하기

1회는 천천히 또박또박, 2·3회는 정상 속도로 따라 말해 보세요.

🎧 ED2-065

1회   2회   3회

① Native Americans were the first people **to live** in America. ✔

아메리카 원주민은 최초로 아메리카에 살았던 사람들입니다.

• to 부정사 : ~하는, ~할

② However, many years later, explorers came **to** America **from** Europe.

하지만 많은 세월이 지난 뒤에, 탐험가들이 유럽에서 아메리카로 건너왔습니다.

• **to A from B** B에서 A로(= from B to A)

③ **While sailing**, he thought he was going to the continent of Asia.

항해를 하면서, 그는 아시아 대륙으로 가고 있다고 생각했습니다.

• **while sailing** = while [he was] sailing

④ But he landed in North America.

하지만 그는 북아메리카에 도착했습니다.

Unit 10 63

ED2-066

단어 쓰기   뜻 쓰기

1

2

3

4

5

6

7

8

9

10

문장 받아쓰기

오디오를 듣고 빈칸에 알맞은 단어를 쓰세요.

1단계 느린 속도로 듣고 받아쓰기

🎧 ED2-067

① But he _____ in North _____ .

② While _____ , he thought he was going to the _____
of Asia.

③ _____ Americans were the first people to _____ in
America.

④ However, many years later, _____ came to America from
_____ .

2단계 정상 속도로 듣고 받아쓰기

🎧 ED2-068

① _____ _____ were the _____ people to
_____ in America.

② While _____ , he _____ he was going to the
_____ of _____ .

③ But he _____ in _____ _____ .

④ However, many years _____ , _____ came to
_____ from _____ .

1

Q: Where did _____ _____?

A: He _____ in North _____.

2

Q: _____ did Columbus _____ from?

A: He _____ from _____.

3

Q: Who were the _____ _____?

A: They were the _____ people to _____ in America.

4

Q: Where did _____ go to _____ from?

A: _____ came to America from _____.

America's Past

_____ _____ were the _____ people to _____ in _____ .

However, many years _____, _____ _____ to America from _____ . One _____ _____ was Christopher Columbus.

_____ _____ from Spain. While _____, he _____ he was _____ to the continent of _____ . But he _____ in _____ America.

He did _____ _____ that.

After Columbus, _____ from different _____ went to _____ .

The Pilgrims

* 종교의 자유를 찾아 미국으로 이주했던 영국 청교도에
관한 표현을 듣고 받아써 봅니다.

핵심단어 따라 말하기

단어를 3회 들려줍니다. 한 번씩 듣고 따라 말해 보세요.

ED2-071

| | | 1회 | 2회 | 3회 |

1 **rule** [ruːl] 　　　　　　　　　동 다스리다, 통치하다 　✔ ○ ○

2 **travel** [trǽvəl] 　　　　　　　동 이주하다, 여행하다 　○ ○ ○

3 **religious** [rilídʒəs] 　　　　　형 종교적인 　○ ○ ○

4 **Pilgrim** [pílgrim] 　　　　　　명 청교도, 순례자 　○ ○ ○

5 **colonist** [kálənist] 　　　　　명 식민지 주민 　○ ○ ○

6 **colony** [káləni] 　　　　　　　명 식민지 　○ ○ ○

7 **church** [tʃəːrtʃ] 　　　　　　　명 교회 　○ ○ ○

8 **difference** [dífərəns] 　　　　명 차이, 다른 점 　○ ○ ○

9 **group** [gruːp] 　　　　　　　　명 집단, 그룹 　○ ○ ○

10 **build** [bild] 　　　　　　　　동 짓다, 건설하다 　○ ○ ○

핵심문장 따라 말하기

1회는 천천히 또박또박, 2·3회는 정상 속도로 따라 말해 보세요.

🎧 ED2-072

1회 2회 3회

① The Pilgrims left England **because of** religious differences with the Church of England.

청교도는 영국 국교회와의 종교적인 차이 때문에 영국을 떠났습니다.

• because of ~ 때문에

② The Pilgrims built **a colony called** Plymouth.

청교도는 플리머스라고 불린 식민지를 세웠습니다.

• a colony called = a colony which[that] was called

③ A colony is **a place ruled** by another country.

식민지는 다른 나라의 지배를 받는 곳입니다.

• a place ruled = a place which[that] is ruled

④ A person **who** lives in a colony is called a colonist.

식민지에 거주하는 사람은 식민지 주민이라고 불립니다.

• who : ~하는 사람

단어 쓰기

뜻 쓰기

1

2

3

4

5

6

7

8

9

10

문장 받아쓰기

오디오를 듣고 빈칸에 알맞은 단어를 쓰세요.

1단계 느린 속도로 듣고 받아쓰기

🎧 ED2-074

❶ A person who lives in a _____ is called a _____.

❷ The _____ built a colony called _____.

❸ A _____ is a place _____ by another country.

❹ The Pilgrims left England because of _____ differences with the _____ of England.

2단계 정상 속도로 듣고 받아쓰기

🎧 ED2-075

❶ The _____ built a _____ called _____.

❷ A person who _____ in a _____ is called a _____.

❸ The _____ left England because of _____ _____ with the _____ of England.

❹ A _____ is a _____ _____ by another _____.

ED2-076~076R

1

Q : Why did the _____ _____ England?

A : Because of _____ _____ with the Church of England.

2

Q : What was the name of the _____ that the _____ _____ on?

A : The name of the _____ the _____ traveled on was the _____.

3

Q : Which _____ _____ Plymouth?

A : _____ ruled _____.

4

Q : What did the Pilgrims _____ as a _____?

A : The _____ built _____ as a colony.

72

The Pilgrims

The _____ were a _____ of people who _____
from _____ to _____ on a ship called the
_____. The Pilgrims _____ England because of
_____ _____ with the _____ of England.
The Pilgrims _____ a _____ called _____.
A _____ is a place _____ by another _____.
Plymouth was _____ by _____. A _____ who
_____ in a colony is called a _____.

Unit 12 Slavery

＊ 미국의 노예제도와 노예제도를 철폐하는 데 영향을 준
남북전쟁에 관한 표현을 듣고 받아써 봅니다.

핵심단어 따라 말하기

단어를 3회 들려줍니다. 한 번씩 듣고 따라 말해 보세요.

🎧 ED2-078

1회　2회　3회

1 **law** [lɔː]　　명 법, 법률　　✔ ○ ○

2 **against** [əɡénst]　　전 ~에 반대하는　　○ ○ ○

3 **force** [fɔːrs]　　동 강제로 ~하게 하다　　○ ○ ○

4 **slavery** [sléivəri]　　명 노예제도　　○ ○ ○

5 **allow** [əláu]　　동 허락하다　　○ ○ ○

6 **freedom** [fríːdəm]　　명 자유　　○ ○ ○

7 **state** [steit]　　명 주(州)　　○ ○ ○

8 **act** [ækt]　　명 행위, 법률　　○ ○ ○

9 **pay** [pei]　　명 보수　　○ ○ ○

10 **war** [wɔːr]　　명 전쟁　　○ ○ ○

핵심문장 따라 말하기

1회는 천천히 또박또박, 2·3회는 정상 속도로 따라 말해 보세요.

🎧 ED2-079

1회 2회 3회

1 **In the United States of America, many states had laws that allowed slavery.**

미국에서는, 많은 주(州)가 노예제도를 허가하는 법을 가지고 있었습니다.

• that : ~하는 것

2 **Many people in the northern part of the country wanted laws against slavery.**

미국 북부 지역의 많은 사람들은 노예제도에 반대하는 법을 원했습니다.

3 **There was a war between them called the Civil War.**

그들 사이에 남북전쟁으로 불리는 전쟁이 일어났습니다.

• between ~ 사이에

4 **After the war ended in 1865, slavery became against the law.**

1865년에 그 전쟁이 끝난 뒤, 노예제도는 법을 위반하는 것이 되었습니다.

• against the law 법에 위반되는, 불법의

단어 받아쓰기

오디오에서 불러주는 단어를 받아쓰고 우리말 뜻을 쓰세요.

ED2-080

단어 쓰기 　　　　　　　　　　　　　　뜻 쓰기

1

2

3

4

5

6

7

8

9

10

1단계 느린 속도로 듣고 받아쓰기

ED2-081

1 There was a _____ between them called the _____ War.

2 In the United States of America, many _____ had laws that allowed _____ .

3 Many people in the _____ part of the country wanted laws _____ slavery.

4 After the war _____ in 1865, _____ became against the _____ .

2단계 정상 속도로 듣고 받아쓰기

ED2-082

1 In the United States of _____ , many _____ had laws that _____ _____ .

2 Many people in the _____ part of the country wanted _____ _____ _____ .

3 There was a _____ between them _____ the _____ _____ .

4 After the _____ _____ in 1865, _____ became _____ the _____ .

①

Q: What is _____?

A: Slavery is the _____ of _____ people to work without _____ and taking away their _____.

②

Q: What did people in the _____ part of the United States _____?

A: They wanted to _____ _____.

③

Q: What did people in the _____ _____ of the United States _____?

A: They wanted _____ _____ _____.

④

Q: What _____ between the _____ part and the _____ part of the United States?

A: The _____ War _____ between them.

Slavery

In the United States of _____, many _____ had _____ that _____ _____. Slavery is the _____ of _____ people to work _____ _____ and _____ away their _____.

Many people in the _____ part of the _____ wanted _____ _____ _____. Many people in the _____ part wanted to _____ _____.

There was a _____ between them called the _____ _____. After the war _____ in 1865, _____ became _____ the _____.

Melody and Rhythm

＊ 멜로디와 리듬을 비교하는 표현을 듣고 받아써 봅니다.

핵심단어 따라 말하기

단어를 3회 들려줍니다. 한 번씩 듣고 따라 말해 보세요.

🎧ED2-085

		1회	2회	3회

1 **note** [nout] 　　　　　　　 명 음, 음표

2 **tap** [tæp] 　　　　　　　 동 박자를 맞추다

3 **rhythm** [ríðəm] 　　　　　　 명 리듬

4 **clap** [klæp] 　　　　　　　 동 박수치다

5 **melody** [mélədi] 　　　　　 명 멜로디

6 **play** [plei] 　　　　　　　 동 연주하다

7 **instrument** [ínstrəmənt] 　 명 악기, 도구

8 **length** [leŋkθ] 　　　　　　 명 길이

9 **group** [gruːp] 　　　　　　 명 집합

10 **toe** [tou] 　　　　　　　 명 발가락

핵심문장 따라 말하기

1회는 천천히 또박또박, 2·3회는 정상 속도로 따라 말해 보세요.

🎧 ED2-086

1회　2회　3회

1 When you sing a song, the part **that** you are singing is the melody.

노래를 부를 때, 여러분이 노래하는 부분이 멜로디입니다.

• that : ~가 …하는 것

2 It is **a group of** notes.

그것은 여러 가지 음의 집합입니다.

• a group of ~의 집단, 무리

3 Melodies have rhythm.

멜로디에는 리듬이 있습니다.

4 The rhythm is the length of the notes.

리듬은 음의 길이입니다.

ED2-087

단어 쓰기   뜻 쓰기

1

2

3

4

5

6

7

8

9

10

1단계 느린 속도로 듣고 받아쓰기

🎧 ED2-088

❶ The _____ is the length of the _____ .

❷ When you _____ a song, the _____ that you are singing is the _____ .

❸ It is a group of _____ .

❹ Melodies have _____ .

2단계 정상 속도로 듣고 받아쓰기

🎧 ED2-089

❶ _____ have _____ .

❷ When you _____ a song, the _____ that you are _____ is the _____ .

❸ The _____ is the _____ of the _____ .

❹ It is a _____ of _____ .

ED2-090~090R

1

Q: What is _____?

A: It is the _____ of the _____.

2

Q: What is it that you play on the _____
or _____ with your _____?

A: It is _____.

3

Q: When you sing a _____, what is the
_____ that you are _____?

A: It is the _____.

4

Q: What can we do with _____ for
_____?

A: We can _____ _____ with
instruments.

Melody and Rhythm

When you sing a _____, the _____ that you are _____ is the _____. It is a _____ of _____. Melodies can be _____ on _____ such as the piano or _____.

_____ have _____. The _____ is the _____ of the _____. It is what you _____ on the _____, _____ with your _____, or _____ with your _____ while a _____ is _____.

Enjoying Music

* 음악 감상의 다양한 예에 관한 표현을 듣고 받아써 봅니다.

핵심단어 따라 말하기

단어를 3회 들려줍니다. 한 번씩 듣고 따라 말해 보세요.

ED2-092

		1회	2회	3회

① **concert** [kánsə(ː)rt] 　명 콘서트, 음악회 ✓ ○ ○

② **learn** [ləːrn] 　동 배우다 ○ ○ ○

③ **listen** [lísn] 　동 듣다 ○ ○ ○

④ **flute** [fluːt] 　명 플루트 ○ ○ ○

⑤ **violin** [vàiəlín] 　명 바이올린 ○ ○ ○

⑥ **even** [íːvən] 　부 심지어, ~조차 ○ ○ ○

⑦ **enjoy** [indʒɔ́i] 　동 즐기다 ○ ○ ○

⑧ **way** [wei] 　명 방법, 길 ○ ○ ○

⑨ **piano** [piǽnou] 　명 피아노 ○ ○ ○

⑩ **guitar** [gitáːr] 　명 기타 ○ ○ ○

핵심문장 따라 말하기

1회는 천천히 또박또박, 2·3회는 정상 속도로 따라 말해 보세요.

🎧 ED2-093

1회 2회 3회

1 **People can enjoy music by listening to it.**

사람들은 음악을 들으며 그것을 즐길 수 있습니다.

• by ~를 통해서

2 **They can go to concerts or listen to music on CDs, computers, and even mobile phones.**

그들은 콘서트에 가거나, CD, 컴퓨터, 심지어는 휴대전화로 음악을 들을 수 있습니다.

• can 〈조동사〉+동사원형 : ~할 수 있다

3 **People also can enjoy music by learning to play instruments such as the piano, guitar, violin, and flute.**

사람들은 또한 피아노와 기타, 바이올린, 그리고 플루트와 같은 악기를 연주하는 법을 배우며 음악을 즐길 수도 있습니다.

• such as ~와 같은

4 **People can learn to make music.**

사람들은 음악을 작곡하는 법을 배울 수 있습니다.

• learn to ~하는 법을 배우다

단어 쓰기　　　　　　　　　뜻 쓰기

1

2

3

4

5

6

7

8

9

10

1단계 느린 속도로 듣고 받아쓰기

ED2-095

❶ People can enjoy _____ by _____ to it.

❷ People can _____ to _____ music.

❸ They can go to _____ or listen to music on CDs, computers, and even _____ _____.

❹ People also can _____ music by learning to _____ _____ such as the piano, guitar, violin, and flute.

2단계 정상 속도로 듣고 받아쓰기

ED2-096

❶ They can _____ to _____ or _____ to music on CDs, computers, and even _____ _____.

❷ People can _____ _____ by _____ to it.

❸ People also can _____ music by _____ to play _____ such as the piano, guitar, violin, and _____.

❹ People can _____ to _____ _____.

ED2-097~097R

❶ Q: Why do we _____ to _____?

A: We go to concerts to _____ to _____.

❷ Q: What can we do by _____ to _____?

A: We can _____ _____.

❸ Q: What is it like to _____ to _____ _____?

A: It is one _____ to _____ _____.

❹ Q: What can we _____ to _____ to _____ music?

A: We can learn to _____ _____.

Enjoying Music

People can _____ _____ by _____ to it. They can

go to _____ or _____ to music on CDs, _____,

and even _____ _____.

People also can _____ music by _____ to _____

_____ such as the _____, _____, _____,

and _____.

People can _____ to _____ _____. Making music

is not _____, but it is one _____ to _____ _____.

Musical Instruments

＊ 다양한 악기 종류와 연주 방법에 관한 표현을 듣고 받아써 봅니다.

핵심단어 따라 말하기

단어를 3회 들려줍니다. 한 번씩 듣고 따라 말해 보세요.

🎧 ED2-099

		1회	2회	3회

1 **bow** [bou] 　　　　　 명 활　　　　　 ✓ ○ ○

2 **mallet** [mǽlit] 　　　　　 명 나무망치　　　　　 ○ ○ ○

3 **percussion** [pərkʌ́ʃən] 　　　　　 명 타악기　　　　　 ○ ○ ○

4 **string** [striŋ] 　　　　　 명 줄, 현　　　　　 ○ ○ ○

5 **shake** [ʃeik] 　　　　　 동 흔들다　　　　　 ○ ○ ○

6 **include** [inklúːd] 　　　　　 동 포함하다　　　　　 ○ ○ ○

7 **crash** [kræʃ] 　　　　　 명 굉음, 요란한 소리　　　　　 ○ ○ ○

8 **blow** [blou] 　　　　　 동 (입으로) 불다　　　　　 ○ ○ ○

9 **strum** [strʌm] 　　　　　 동 치다, 퉁기다　　　　　 ○ ○ ○

10 **pluck** [plʌk] 　　　　　 동 뜯다, 퉁기다　　　　　 ○ ○ ○

핵심문장 따라 말하기

1회는 천천히 또박또박, 2·3회는 정상 속도로 따라 말해 보세요.

🎧 ED2-100

1회   2회   3회

1 **You shake percussion instruments or hit them with your hands, a stick, or a mallet.**

여러분은 타악기를 흔들거나 손, 막대, 또는 나무망치로 타악기를 칩니다.

2 **Instruments with strings are called stringed instruments.**

줄이 달린 악기는 현악기라고 불립니다.

• **be called** ~라고 불리다

3 **You play them either by strumming or plucking them with your fingers or by playing them with a bow.**

여러분은 손가락으로 줄을 치거나 퉁겨서, 또는 활을 이용해서 현악기를 연주합니다.

• **either A or B** A 아니면 B

4 **You play wind instruments by blowing air into them.**

관악기는 악기 속으로 공기를 불어넣어 연주합니다.

• **blow air into** ~ 안으로 공기를 불어넣다

단어 쓰기　　　　　　　　　뜻 쓰기

1

2

3

4

5

6

7

8

9

10

1단계 느린 속도로 듣고 받아쓰기

ED2-102

1 Instruments with _____ are called _____ instruments.

2 You play them either by _____ or _____ them with your fingers or by playing them with a bow.

3 You play _____ instruments by _____ air into them.

4 You _____ percussion instruments or _____ them with your hands, a stick, or a mallet.

2단계 정상 속도로 듣고 받아쓰기

ED2-103

1 You play _____ by _____ into them.

2 Instruments with _____ are called _____ _____.

3 You play them either by _____ or _____ them with your _____ or by playing them with a _____.

4 You _____ instruments or _____ them with your hands, a _____, or a _____.

ED2-104~104R

❶ Q: What do we use to _____ the _____?

A: We _____ our _____ and a _____.

❷ Q: How do we play _____
_____?

A: We play them by _____ or _____
them.

❸ Q: What kind of instruments are the _____
and _____?

A: They are _____ _____.

❹ Q: How do we _____ _____
_____?

A: We play them by _____ _____ into
them.

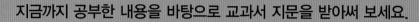
Musical Instruments

You _____ _____ instruments or _____ them with your _____, a _____, or a _____. Percussion instruments _____ the _____, _____, tambourine, and _____. When you _____ _____ together, they make a _____ like a loud _____. Instruments with _____ are called _____ _____. You play them either by _____ or _____ them with your _____ or by playing them with a _____. The _____, _____, and _____ are stringed instruments. You play _____ instruments by _____ _____ into them. Some _____ _____ made of _____ are called _____. Others made of _____ are called _____ _____. The _____, _____, and _____ are wind instruments.

Keyboard and Electronic Instruments

* 건반악기와 전자악기의 특징 및 연주 방법에 관한 표현을
듣고 받아써 봅니다.

핵심단어 따라 말하기

단어를 3회 들려줍니다. 한 번씩 듣고 따라 말해 보세요.

🎧 ED2-106

1회　2회　3회

① **note** [nout]　　　　　　　　　　명 음, 음표　　✔ ◯ ◯

② **keyboard** [kí:bɔ̀:rd]　　　　　　명 건반, 키보드　　◯ ◯ ◯

③ **nowadays** [náuədèiz]　　　　　부 요즘　　◯ ◯ ◯

④ **popular** [pápjələr]　　　　　　형 인기 있는　　◯ ◯ ◯

⑤ **pick** [pik]　　　　　　　　　　명 피크　　◯ ◯ ◯

⑥ **electronic** [ilektránik]　　　　형 전자의　　◯ ◯ ◯

⑦ **electricity** [ilektrísəti]　　　명 전기　　◯ ◯ ◯

⑧ **organ** [ɔ́:rgən]　　　　　　　　명 오르간　　◯ ◯ ◯

⑨ **mean** [mi:n]　　　　　　　　　동 의미하다　　◯ ◯ ◯

⑩ **electric** [iléktrik]　　　　　　형 전기의　　◯ ◯ ◯

핵심문장 따라 말하기

1회는 천천히 또박또박, 2·3회는 정상 속도로 따라 말해 보세요.

ED2-107

1회   2회   3회

① Some musical instruments like the piano and organ use a keyboard.

피아노와 오르간 같은 일부 악기는 건반을 사용합니다.

② One person can play many notes **at the same time** on a keyboard instrument.

건반악기로는 한 사람이 많은 음을 동시에 연주할 수 있습니다.

• at the same time 동시에

③ Musical instruments that use electricity **are called** electronic instruments.

전기를 이용하는 악기는 전자악기라고 불립니다.

• be called ~라고 불리다

④ The electric guitar is **one of the most popular of these.**

전기 기타는 이 중에서 가장 인기 있는 것 중의 하나입니다.

• one of the + 최상급 + of + 복수명사 : ~ 중에서 가장 …한 것 중의 하나

단어 쓰기　　　　　　　　　　뜻 쓰기

1

2

3

4

5

6

7

8

9

10

문장 받아쓰기

오디오를 듣고 빈칸에 알맞은 단어를 쓰세요.

1단계 느린 속도로 듣고 받아쓰기

🎧 ED2-109

❶ One person can play many _____ at the same time on a _____ instrument.

❷ Some musical instruments like the _____ and organ use a _____ .

❸ The _____ guitar is one of the most _____ of these.

❹ _____ instruments that use _____ are called _____ instruments.

2단계 정상 속도로 듣고 받아쓰기

🎧 ED2-110

❶ _____ _____ that use _____ are called _____ _____ .

❷ The _____ guitar is one of the _____ _____ of these.

❸ Some musical _____ like the _____ and _____ use a _____ .

❹ One person can _____ many _____ at the _____ time on a _____ instrument.

1

Q: Nowadays, when people talk about a _____, what are they _____ about?

A: They are talking about an _____ _____.

2

Q: What is a _____ of a _____ instrument?

A: One person can _____ many _____ at the _____ time on it.

3

Q: What do we _____ the _____ and _____?

A: We call them _____ _____.

4

Q: Is the _____ _____ only played with a _____?

A: No. It also can be _____ with _____.

Keyboard and Electronic Instruments

Some _____ _____ like the piano and _____ use a

_____. These are called _____ _____.

One person can _____ many _____ at the _____

_____ on a _____ instrument: you can play as _____

_____ as you have _____ all at the _____ time.

The harpsichord is a very _____ _____ of keyboard

while _____ _____ instruments are _____ ones.

_____, when people _____ about a keyboard, they often

_____ an _____ _____.

Musical instruments that _____ _____ are called

_____ _____. The electric _____ is one of the

_____ _____ of

these. It is a _____

_____ usually

_____ with a _____

and sometimes with

_____.

Tahitian Landscape

※ 폴 고갱의 그림 〈타히티 섬의 풍경〉에서 따뜻한 색을 사용한
의도에 관한 표현을 듣고 받아써 봅니다.

핵심단어 따라 말하기

단어를 3회 들려줍니다. 한 번씩 듣고 따라 말해 보세요.

🎧 ED2-113

| | | 1회 | 2회 | 3회 |

1 **warm** [wɔːrm] 형 따뜻한 ✔ ○ ○

2 **clear** [kliər] 형 맑은, 깨끗한 ○ ○ ○

3 **bright** [brait] 형 밝은 ○ ○ ○

4 **landscape** [lǽndskèip] 명 풍경 ○ ○ ○

5 **painting** [péintiŋ] 명 그림 ○ ○ ○

6 **intention** [inténʃən] 명 의도 ○ ○ ○

7 **look** [luk] 동 보다 ○ ○ ○

8 **point** [pɔint] 동 가리키다 ○ ○ ○

9 **find** [faind] 동 발견하다, 찾다 ○ ○ ○

10 **feel** [fiːl] 동 느끼다 ○ ○ ○

핵심문장 따라 말하기

1회는 천천히 또박또박, 2·3회는 정상 속도로 따라 말해 보세요.

🎧 ED2-114

1회   2회   3회

1 In Paul Gauguin's *Tahitian Lanscape*, **as** you can see, Gauguin used warm colors.

여러분이 보시다시피, 폴 고갱은 그의 그림 〈타히티 섬의 풍경〉에서 따뜻한 색을 사용했습니다.

- **as** 〈접속사〉 : ~하다시피, ~하는 대로

2 Can you feel his intention?

여러분은 그의 의도가 느껴지나요?

3 He wanted to **make us feel** the hot sun and **see** the bright and clear sky.

그는 우리가 뜨거운 태양을 느끼고, 밝고 맑은 하늘을 볼 수 있기를 원했습니다.

- **make** + 목적어 + 동사원형 : ~가 …하게 하다

4 Red, yellow, and orange are warm colors.

빨간색, 노란색, 그리고 주황색은 따뜻한 색입니다.

단어 쓰기   뜻 쓰기

1

2

3

4

5

6

7

8

9

10

1단계 느린 속도로 듣고 받아쓰기

🎧 ED2-116

❶ Can you feel his   ?

❷ Red, yellow, and orange are   .

❸ In Paul Gauguin's *Tahitian*   , as you can   ,
Gauguin used   colors.

❹ He wanted to make us   the   sun and see
the bright and   sky.

2단계 정상 속도로 듣고 받아쓰기

🎧 ED2-117

❶ In Paul Gauguin's *Tahitian*   , as you can   ,
Gauguin   .

❷ Red,   , and orange are   .

❸ He wanted to make us   the   sun and
see the   and   sky.

❹ Can you   his   ?

1

Q: What can we feel through Gauguin's
_____ of _____ _____?

A: We can _____ his _____.

2

Q: In *Tahitian* _____, what _____
did Gauguin _____?

A: Gauguin _____ _____ colors.

3

Q: What did Gauguin _____ us to
_____ by using _____ colors?

A: He _____ us to feel the _____
_____.

4

Q: What are _____ _____?

A: _____, _____, and _____ are
warm colors.

Tahitian Landscape

What do you _____ from this _____?

In Paul Gauguin's *Tahitian* _____, as you can _____,

Gauguin _____ _____ _____. Can you _____

his _____? He wanted to make us _____ the

_____ _____ and see the _____ and _____

_____.

_____, yellow, and _____ are _____ _____.

Now _____ at Gauguin's _____ and _____ at all

the _____ colors you can _____.

Paul Gauguin, *Tahitian Landscape* (1891)

Blue Atmosphere

* 헬렌 프랑켄탈러의 그림 〈Blue Atmosphere〉의 독특한
색 표현에 관한 표현을 듣고 받아써 봅니다.

핵심단어 따라 말하기

단어를 3회 들려줍니다. 한 번씩 듣고 따라 말해 보세요.

🎧 ED2-120

| | | 1회 | 2회 | 3회 |

❶ **artist** [ɑ́ːrtist] 　　　　명 예술가, 화가 ✓ ○ ○

❷ **push** [puʃ] 　　　　동 밀다 ○ ○ ○

❸ **atmosphere** [ǽtməsfiər] 　　　　명 분위기, 대기 ○ ○ ○

❹ **include** [inklúːd] 　　　　동 포함하다 ○ ○ ○

❺ **fiery** [fáiəri] 　　　　형 불타는 듯한, 불 같은 ○ ○ ○

❻ **seem** [siːm] 　　　　동 보이다, ~인 것 같다 ○ ○ ○

❼ **cool** [kuːl] 　　　　형 시원한 ○ ○ ○

❽ **deep** [diːp] 　　　　형 깊은, 짙은 ○ ○ ○

❾ **use** [juːz] 　　　　동 사용하다 ○ ○ ○

❿ **Earth** [əːrθ] 　　　　명 지구, 세상 ○ ○ ○

핵심문장 따라 말하기

1회는 천천히 또박또박, 2·3회는 정상 속도로 따라 말해 보세요.

🎧 ED2-121

1회　　2회　　3회

① Some artists only use colors in their paintings **without** including people or things.

어떤 화가는 자신의 그림에, 사람이나 사물을 포함하지 않고, 오직 색만 사용합니다.

• without ~하지 않고, ~없이

② Helen Frankenthaler's *Blue Atmosphere* is a painting **made up** only **of** colors.

헬렌 프랑켄탈러의 〈푸른 기운〉은 오직 색만으로 구성된 그림입니다.

• made up of ~로 구성된

③ **Though** the artist called this painting *Blue Atmosphere*, there is **a lot of** red in it.

화가는 이 그림을 〈푸른 기운〉이라고 불렀지만, 그 그림에는 빨간색이 많이 있습니다.

• though 〈접속사〉 : ~임에도 불구하고(= although, even though)　• a lot of 많은 ~

④ The fiery red **seems to** be pushing back the cool and deep blue.

불타는 듯한 빨간색은 시원하고 짙은 파란색을 밀어내는 것처럼 보입니다.

• seem to ~인 것처럼 보이다

단어 쓰기   뜻 쓰기

1

2

3

4

5

6

7

8

9

10

문장 받아쓰기

오디오를 듣고 빈칸에 알맞은 단어를 쓰세요.

1단계 〉 느린 속도로 듣고 받아쓰기

🎧 ED2-123

1 Helen Frankenthaler's _____ *Atmosphere* is a _____ made up only of _____.

2 Though the _____ called this painting *Blue* _____, there is a lot of _____ in it.

3 The _____ red seems to be _____ back the cool and deep _____.

4 Some _____ only use colors in their paintings without _____ people or _____.

2단계 〉 정상 속도로 듣고 받아쓰기

🎧 ED2-124

1 The _____ red _____ to be _____ back the cool and _____ _____.

2 Though the _____ called this _____ _____ _____, there is a lot of _____ in it.

3 Helen Frankenthaler's _____ *Atmosphere* is a _____ _____ up only of _____.

4 Some _____ only _____ _____ in their paintings without _____ people or _____.

① Q: What does _____ _____ _____ like?

A: It looks like the _____ _____ is _____ back the _____.

② Q: What can we _____ in _____ *Atmosphere*?

A: We can _____ there is a lot of _____ in it.

③ Q: What is *Blue* _____ _____ up of?

A: _____ _____ is a _____ made up only of _____.

④ Q: Can we _____ _____ including _____ or things?

A: Yes. Some artists _____ _____ _____ in their paintings.

Blue Atmosphere

Some _____ only _____ _____ in their paintings
_____ including _____ or _____.
Helen Frankenthaler's _____ _____ is a _____
made up only of _____. Though the _____ _____
this _____ *Blue Atmosphere*, there is a _____ of
_____ in it. The _____ red _____ to be _____
back the cool and _____ _____. What _____
would you _____ this _____?

Helen Frankenthaler, *Blue Atmosphere* (1963)

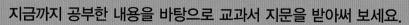

Lines

＊ 선의 다양한 종류에 관한 표현을 듣고 받아써 봅니다.

핵심단어 따라 말하기

단어를 3회 들려줍니다. 한 번씩 듣고 따라 말해 보세요.

🎧 ED2-127

		1회	2회	3회

1 **line** [lain] 　　　　　　　　　 명 선 ✓ ○ ○

2 **straight** [streit] 　　　　　　 형 곧은, 쭉 뻗은 ○ ○ ○

3 **circle** [sə́:rkl] 　　　　　　　 명 원, 동그라미 ○ ○ ○

4 **spiral** [spáiərəl] 　　　　　　 형 나선형의 ○ ○ ○

5 **bend** [bend] 　　　　　　　　 동 구부리다, 구부러지다 ○ ○ ○

6 **vertical** [və́:rtikəl] 　　　　　 형 수직의 ○ ○ ○

7 **horizontal** [hɔ̀(:)rəzántəl] 　 형 수평의 ○ ○ ○

8 **diagonal** [daiǽgənəl] 　　　 형 대각선의, 사선의 ○ ○ ○

9 **zigzag** [zígzæg] 　　　　　　 명 지그재그형 ○ ○ ○

10 **direction** [dirékʃən] 　　　　 명 방향 ○ ○ ○

핵심문장 따라 말하기

1회는 천천히 또박또박, 2·3회는 정상 속도로 따라 말해 보세요.

🎧 ED2-128

1회　2회　3회

① **Lines do not have to be just straight.**

선이 반드시 딱 일직선이어야 할 필요는 없습니다.

• do not have to ~할 필요 없다

② **They are straight lines, but they point in different directions.**

그것들은 직선이지만, 서로 다른 방향을 향합니다.

③ **The lines that are leaning are called diagonal lines.**

기울어져 있는 선은 대각선이라고 불립니다.

• that : ~하는 것

④ **The lines that bend a little are called curved lines.**

약간 구부러진 선은 곡선이라고 불립니다.

• be called ~라고 불리다

단어 쓰기

뜻 쓰기

1

2

3

4

5

6

7

8

9

10

문장 받아쓰기

오디오를 듣고 빈칸에 알맞은 단어를 쓰세요.

1단계 느린 속도로 듣고 받아쓰기

🎧 ED2-130

1 The lines that are _____ are called _____ lines.

2 The lines that _____ a little are called _____ lines.

3 They are straight lines, but they _____ in different _____ .

4 Lines do not _____ to be just _____ .

2단계 정상 속도로 듣고 받아쓰기

🎧 ED2-131

1 Lines do not _____ to be _____ _____ .

2 They are _____ lines, but they _____ in _____ _____ .

3 The lines that _____ a little are called _____ _____ .

4 The lines that are _____ are called _____ _____ .

1

Q: When a line _____ in many _____, what do we call it?

A: We _____ it a _____.

2

Q: What do we call the _____ that _____ a little?

A: We call them _____ _____.

3

Q: What are _____ _____?

A: The lines that are _____ are _____ lines.

4

Q: How does the line of a _____ _____?

A: It _____ _____ the way _____.

Lines

_____ do not _____ to be just _____. They

are _____ lines, but they _____ in _____

_____. The lines that point _____ and _____

are called _____ _____. The lines that point

_____ to _____ are _____ _____. The

lines that are _____ are called _____ _____.

Look at the _____ _____. It is more _____ or

_____ _____ to a _____ line because it

_____ in more _____.

Here are some _____ _____. These lines are _____.

The lines that _____ a little are called _____ _____.

The line that _____ all the _____ _____ is called

a _____. The line that _____ _____ _____

itself is called a _____.

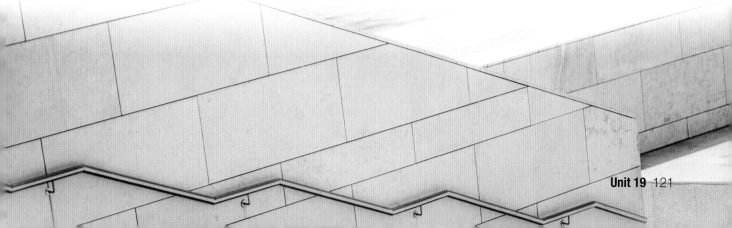

Drawing with Lines

* 선으로만 구성한 그림에 관한 표현을 듣고 받아써 봅니다.

핵심단어 따라 말하기

단어를 3회 들려줍니다. 한 번씩 듣고 따라 말해 보세요.

🎧 ED2-134

			1회	2회	3회
①	**neck** [nek]	명 목	✓		
②	**curved** [kəːrvd]	형 곡선의, 구부러진			
③	**graceful** [gréisfəl]	형 우아한			
④	**drawing** [drɔ́ːiŋ]	명 그림, 소묘			
⑤	**painting** [péintiŋ]	명 그림			
⑥	**French** [frenʧ]	형 프랑스의, 프랑스인의			
⑦	**swan** [swɑn]	명 백조			
⑧	**spiral** [spáiərəl]	형 나선형의			
⑨	**curve** [kəːrv]	동 구부러지다			
⑩	**inside** [insáid]	부 안으로 전 ~ 안에			

핵심문장 따라 말하기

1회는 천천히 또박또박, 2·3회는 정상 속도로 따라 말해 보세요.

ED2-135

1회 2회 3회

① There is **a picture made** only from lines.

오로지 선으로만 구성된 그림이 있습니다.

• **a picture made** = a picture that [which] is made

② Curved lines can **seem graceful**.

곡선은 우아해 보일 수 있습니다.

• **seem** + 형용사: ~해 보이다

③ In the painting, called *Shell No.1*, do you see one type of line that **stands out** more than the others?

〈제1의 껍데기〉라는 그림에서, 다른 선보다 훨씬 더 두드러지는 유형의 선이 보이나요?

• **stand out** 두드러지다, 뛰어나다

④ A spiral line is a line that **keeps curving** inside itself.

나선은 안으로 계속 구부러져 들어가는 선입니다.

• **keep -ing** 계속 ~하다

Unit 20 123

단어 쓰기   뜻 쓰기

1

2

3

4

5

6

7

8

9

10

1단계 느린 속도로 듣고 받아쓰기

ED2-137

❶ _____ lines can seem _____ .

❷ In the _____, called *Shell No.1*, do you see one type of line that _____ _____ more than the others?

❸ A _____ line is a line that keeps _____ inside itself.

❹ There is a _____ made only from _____ .

2단계 정상 속도로 듣고 받아쓰기

ED2-138

❶ There is a _____ _____ only from _____ .

❷ A _____ line is a line that _____ _____ inside itself.

❸ _____ lines can _____ _____ .

❹ In the _____, called *Shell No.1*, do you see one _____ of line that _____ _____ more than the others?

ED2-139~139R

1

Q: What type of _____ can you see from the _____ of the _____?

A: _____ _____.

2

Q: What did Matisse _____ in his _____, *The Swan*?

A: He _____ used _____.

3

Q: What is a _____ _____?

A: A line that _____ _____ _____ itself is a _____ line.

4

Q: What _____ did O'Keeffe _____ in *Shell No.1*?

A: She used a _____ _____.

126

ED2-140~140R

Drawing with Lines

There is a _____ made only from _____. The _____, called *The* _____, is by French _____ Henri Matisse. What type of _____ does Matisse _____ for the _____ of the _____? _____ _____ can _____ _____. _____ for some of the other curved lines in the _____.

There is a _____ by American _____ Georgia O'Keeffe. _____ for the _____ on the Internet. In the _____, called _____ *No.1*, do you see one _____ of line that _____ _____ more than the others? Do you _____ the _____ lines? A _____ _____ is a line that _____ _____ _____ itself.

Henri Matisse, *The Swan* (1931)

Georgia O'Keeffe, *Shell No.1* (1928)

최신 개정 미국교과서로 독해 실력을 쑥쑥!
미국교과서 READING 시리즈!

| 유치~초등 초급 | 초등 초급 | 초등 중급 | 초등 고급 | 중등 이상 |

단계	Early (전 3권)	Starter (전 3권)	Easy (전 3권)	Basic (전 3권)	Advanced (전 3권)
대상	유치 ~ 초등 초급	초등 초급	초등 중급	초등 고급	중등
특징	기초 어휘와 패턴 문장으로 리딩 시작	흥미로운 주제로 픽션&논픽션을 골고루	교과서 지식과 독해 실력을 동시에 쌓기 (논픽션)		
난이도 word counting	30~40단어	40~60단어	60~80단어	90~120단어	130~180단어

교재 특징 ▶

- 최신 개정 미국교과서 커리큘럼 **반영**
- 학생들의 수준에 꼭 맞는 단계별 리딩 학습
- 지문을 완전히 소화하도록 하는 풍부한 문제풀이!
- 완벽하고 철저한 학습을 돕는 부가 학습 자료 제공!

영어 실력 수직 상승을 위한 미국교과서 듣기 & 받아쓰기 단계별 프로그램

Level
2

미국교과서
리스닝 with
DICTATION

정답 및 해석

길벗스쿨

Dinosaurs

| Step 1 | 단어 받아쓰기 | p. 10 |

❶ skull — 두개골, 해골
❷ hatch — 부화하다, 알에서 나오다
❸ leg — 다리
❹ develop — 성장하다, 발달하다
❺ limb — 팔다리, 다리
❻ nest — 둥지
❼ dinosaur — 공룡
❽ lay — 알을 낳다
❾ walk — 걷다
❿ hole — 구멍

| Step 2 | 문장 받아쓰기 | p. 11 |

1단계 ▶ 느린 속도로 듣고 받아쓰기

❶ All dinosaurs laid eggs.
❷ Dinosaur skulls had large holes.
❸ Dinosaurs all had four limbs.
❹ Some of the largest skulls were almost as long as a car.

2단계 ▶ 정상 속도로 듣고 받아쓰기

❶ Some of the largest skulls were almost as long as a car.
❷ All dinosaurs laid eggs.
❸ Dinosaurs all had four limbs.
❹ Dinosaur skulls had large holes.

| Step 3 | 대화문 받아쓰기 | p. 12 |

❶ Q : What did the holes in dinosaur skulls do?

A : They made the skulls lighter.
❷ Q : Why did dinosaurs need nests?
A : Because they laid eggs in nests.
❸ Q : How many limbs did dinosaurs have?
A : They had four limbs.
❹ Q : What happened to the baby dinosaurs until they were ready to hatch?
A : They developed in their eggs.

＊대화문 받아쓰기 해석

❶ Q : 공룡의 두개골에 있는 구멍은 어떤 역할을 했나요?
A : 그것들은 두개골을 가볍게 해주었습니다.
❷ Q : 공룡은 왜 둥지가 필요했나요?
A : 그들은 둥지에 알을 낳기 때문입니다.
❸ Q : 공룡은 얼마나 많은 다리를 가지고 있었나요?
A : 그것들은 네 개의 다리를 가지고 있었습니다.
❹ Q : 새끼 공룡들이 알에서 나올 준비가 될 때까지 그들에게 무슨 일이 일어났나요?
A : 그들은 알 속에서 계속 성장했습니다.

| Step 4 | 교과서 받아쓰기 | p. 13 |

Dinosaurs

Dinosaurs all had four limbs. But many of them walked on two legs.
Dinosaur skulls had large holes. These holes made their skulls lighter. Some of the largest skulls were almost as long as a car.
All dinosaurs laid eggs–some in nests just like birds do today. The baby developed in the egg until it was ready to hatch.

＊지문 해석

공룡

공룡은 모두 4개의 다리를 가지고 있었습니다. 그러나 많은 공룡이 두 다리로 걸어 다녔지요.
공룡의 두개골에는 커다란 구멍이 있었습니다. 이 구멍은 공룡의 두개골을 가볍게 해주었습니다. 가장 큰 두개골 중 몇몇은 거의 자동차만큼 길었어요.
모든 공룡은 알을 낳았는데, 어떤 공룡은 오늘날 새들이 둥지에서 알을 낳듯이 알을 낳았지요. 새끼는 알에서 나올 준비가 될 때까지 알 속에서 계속 성장했답니다.

Science

Step 1 단어 받아쓰기　　p. 16

1 variety　　다양성
2 truth　　진실, 사실
3 search　　탐구, 조사
4 mystery　　미스터리
5 discover　　발견하다
6 understand　　이해하다
7 universe　　우주
8 knowledge　　지식
9 tiny　　아주 작은
10 material　　재료, 물질

Step 2 문장 받아쓰기　　p. 17

1단계 느린 속도로 듣고 받아쓰기

1 Scientists also study the mysteries of space.
2 Science is the search for truth and knowledge.
3 Scientists study a huge variety of things and discover new facts.
4 It helps us understand life, the universe, and almost everything.

2단계 정상 속도로 듣고 받아쓰기

1 It helps us understand life, the universe, and almost everything.
2 Science is the search for truth and knowledge.
3 Scientists also study the mysteries of space.
4 Scientists study a huge variety of things and discover new facts.

Step 3 대화문 받아쓰기　　p. 18

1 Q : What is science the search for?
　A : Science is the search for truth and knowledge.
2 Q : What do scientists study?
　A : Scientists study a huge variety of things.
3 Q : What are atoms?
　A : Atoms are the things that make up everything around us.
4 Q : What does science help us do?
　A : Science helps us understand life and the universe.

＊ 대화문 받아쓰기 해석

1 Q : 과학은 무엇에 대한 추구입니까?
　A : 과학은 진실과 지식에 대한 추구입니다.
2 Q : 과학자들은 무엇을 연구하나요?
　A : 과학자들은 매우 다양한 것들을 연구합니다.
3 Q : 원자란 무엇인가요?
　A : 원자란 우리를 둘러싼 모든 것을 구성하는 물질입니다.
4 Q : 과학은 우리가 무엇을 하도록 돕나요?
　A : 과학은 우리가 생명과 우주를 이해할 수 있도록 돕습니다.

Step 4 교과서 받아쓰기　　p. 19

Science

Science is the search for truth and knowledge. It helps us understand life, the universe, and almost everything.

Scientists study a huge variety of things and discover new facts. They studied atoms and discovered that atoms are the tiniest objects and make up everything around us. Scientists also study the mysteries of space.

There is life science, physical science, Earth and space science, material science, etc.

과학

과학은 진실과 지식에 대한 추구입니다. 과학은 우리가 생명과 우주, 그리고 거의 모든 것에 대해서 이해할 수 있도록 돕습니다.

과학자들은 매우 다양한 것들을 연구하며 새로운 사실을 발견합니다. 그들은 원자를 연구해서, 원자가 우리를 둘러싼 모든 것을 구성하는 가장 작은 물질이라는 사실을 발견해 냈습니다. 과학자들은 또한 우주의 미스터리도 연구합니다.

과학에는 생명 과학, 물리 과학, 지구 및 우주 과학, 재료 과학 등이 있습니다.

Unit 03

Advances in Science

| Step 1 | 단어 받아쓰기 | p. 22 |

❶ solve — 해결하다, 풀다
❷ recommend — 제안하다
❸ invention — 발명(품)
❹ pose — 제기하다
❺ experiment — 실험
❻ discovery — 발견
❼ influence — 영향을 주다
❽ thinker — 사상가, 생각하는 사람
❾ begin — 시작하다
❿ history — 역사

| Step 2 | 문장 받아쓰기 | p. 23 |

1단계 느린 속도로 듣고 받아쓰기

❶ Many scientists have been influenced by Aristotle.

❷ Science begins with problems.
❸ They wanted to solve the problems that life posed.
❹ The scientists made many great inventions and discoveries.

2단계 정상 속도로 듣고 받아쓰기

❶ The scientists made many great inventions and discoveries.
❷ Many scientists have been influenced by Aristotle.
❸ They wanted to solve the problems that life posed.
❹ Science begins with problems.

| Step 3 | 대화문 받아쓰기 | p. 24 |

❶ Q: What did Aristotle recommend?
   A: He recommended that people carry out experiments to test their ideas.
❷ Q: How did we get great inventions and discoveries?
   A: The scientists made them.
❸ Q: What were the great scientists like?
   A: They were all thinkers.
❹ Q: What did scientists want to do?
   A: They wanted to solve the problems that life posed.

* 대화문 받아쓰기 해석

❶ Q: 아리스토텔레스는 무엇을 제안했나요?
   A: 그는 사람들이 그들의 생각을 시험해 보기 위해 실험을 해 볼 것을 제안했습니다.
❷ Q: 우리는 어떻게 위대한 발명과 발견을 얻었습니까?
   A: 과학자들이 그것들을 이뤄냈습니다.
❸ Q: 위대한 과학자들은 무엇과 같았습니까?
   A: 그들은 모두 사상가였습니다.
❹ Q: 과학자들은 무엇을 하고 싶어 했나요?
   A: 그들은 인생이 제기한 문제를 해결하고 싶어 했습니다.

3

Advances in Science

Science begins with problems.
The great scientists were all thinkers. They wanted to solve the problems that life posed. The scientists made many great inventions and discoveries, which have changed the course of history.
More than 2,000 years ago, the Greek thinker Aristotle recommended that people look at nature and carry out experiments to test their ideas. Many scientists have been influenced by Aristotle.

＊지문 해석

과학의 발달

과학은 문제로부터 시작됩니다.
위대한 과학자들은 모두 사상가였습니다. 그들은 인생이 제기한 문제를 해결하고 싶어 했습니다. 그 과학자들은 수많은 위대한 발명과 발견을 이뤄냈으며, 그것들은 역사의 흐름을 변화시켜 왔습니다.
2,000여 년 전에, 그리스의 사상가 아리스토텔레스는 사람들이 자연을 바라보고 그들의 생각을 시험해 보기 위해 실험을 해볼 것을 제안하였습니다. 많은 과학자들은 아리스토텔레스의 영향을 받았습니다.

Unit 04

Leonardo da Vinci and Galileo Galilei

❶ painter　　　　화가
❷ prove　　　　　증명하다
❸ technology　　기술
❹ parachute　　　낙하산
❺ inventor　　　　발명가
❻ telescope　　　망원경
❼ instrument　　　악기
❽ unfortunately　불행하게도
❾ plan　　　　　　도면, 설계도, 계획
❿ astronomer　　천문학자

1단계　느린 속도로 듣고 받아쓰기

❶ Galileo Galilei was an astronomer and instrument maker.
❷ Leonardo da Vinci was a painter, scientist, and inventor.
❸ He drew plans for helicopters, airplanes, and parachutes.
❹ Unfortunately, the technology of his time was not good enough to build any of them.

2단계　정상 속도로 듣고 받아쓰기

❶ Leonardo da Vinci was a painter, scientist, and inventor.
❷ He drew plans for helicopters, airplanes, and parachutes.
❸ Unfortunately, the technology of his time was not good enough to build any of them.
❹ Galileo Galilei was an astronomer and instrument maker.

❶ Q: What did Galileo Galilei prove about the earth?
　 A: He proved that the earth moves around the sun.
❷ Q: How did Galileo Galilei prove the fact about the earth?
　 A: He looked at the solar system through a telescope.

❸ Q : Did Leonardo da Vinci build the helicopters that he designed?

A : No. The technology of his time was not good enough to build them.

❹ Q : What did Leonardo da Vinci draw?

A : He drew plans for helicopters, airplanes, and parachutes.

* 대화문 받아쓰기 해석

❶ Q : 갈릴레오 갈릴레이는 지구에 대해 무엇을 증명해 냈나요?

A : 그는 지구가 태양의 주위를 돈다는 사실을 증명해 냈습니다.

❷ Q : 갈릴레오 갈릴레이는 지구에 대한 사실을 어떻게 증명해 냈나요?

A : 그는 망원경을 통해 태양계를 관찰했습니다.

❸ Q : 레오나르도 다빈치는 그가 설계한 헬리콥터를 만들어 냈나요?

A : 아니요. 그가 살았던 당시의 기술은 그것들을 만들어 낼 만큼 훌륭하지 않았습니다.

❹ Q : 레오나르도 다빈치는 무엇을 그렸나요?

A : 그는 헬리콥터, 비행기, 그리고 낙하산의 설계도를 그렸습니다.

Step 4 　교과서 받아쓰기　p. 31

Leonardo da Vinci and Galileo Galilei
Leonardo da Vinci (1452-1519) was a painter, scientist, and inventor. He drew plans for helicopters, airplanes, and parachutes. Unfortunately, the technology of his time was not good enough to build any of them.
Galileo Galilei (1564-1642) was an astronomer and instrument maker. He proved that the earth moves around the sun by looking at the solar system through a telescope.

* 지문 해석

레오나르도 다빈치와 갈릴레오 갈릴레이
레오나르도 다빈치(1452-1519)는 화가이자 과학자, 그리고 발명가였습니다. 그는 헬리콥터, 비행기, 그리고 낙하산의 설계도를 그렸습니다. 불행하게도, 그가 살았던 당시의 기술은

그것들 중 어느 하나라도 만들어 낼 만큼 훌륭하지 않았습니다.
갈릴레오 갈릴레이(1564-1642)는 천문학자이자 악기제조자였습니다. 그는 망원경을 통해 태양계를 관찰하면서 지구가 태양의 주위를 돈다는 사실을 증명해 냈습니다.

Unit 05

Isaac Newton and Thomas Edison

Step 1 　단어 받아쓰기　p. 34

❶	deaf	귀가 들리지 않는
❷	suffer	고통 받다, 괴로워하다
❸	mathematician	수학자
❹	force	힘
❺	planet	행성
❻	realize	깨닫다
❼	light bulb	전구
❽	gravity	중력
❾	physicist	물리학자
❿	orbit	궤도

Step 2 　문장 받아쓰기　p. 35

1단계 느린 속도로 듣고 받아쓰기

❶ Thomas Edison was an inventor.

❷ At 12, he suffered from scarlet fever and became deaf.

❸ Isaac Newton was a physicist and mathematician.

❹ He studied forces and light.

2단계 정상 속도로 듣고 받아쓰기

❶ He studied forces and light.

❷ Isaac Newton was a physicist and mathematician.

❸ Thomas Edison was an inventor.

❹ At 12, he suffered from scarlet fever and became deaf.

| Step 3 | 대화문 받아쓰기 | p. 36 |

❶ Q: Who was Thomas Edison?
   A: He was an inventor.
❷ Q: What did Thomas Edison invent?
   A: He invented more than 1,000 things, including light bulbs and batteries.
❸ Q: Who was Isaac Newton?
   A: He was a physicist and mathematician.
❹ Q: What is gravity?
   A: Gravity is a force that keeps the planets in orbit around the sun.

＊대화문 받아쓰기 해석

❶ Q: 토머스 에디슨은 누구였나요?
   A: 그는 발명가였습니다.
❷ Q: 토머스 에디슨은 무엇을 발명했나요?
   A: 그는 전구와 건전지를 포함해 1,000가지 이상의 물건들을 발명했습니다.
❸ Q: 아이작 뉴턴은 누구였나요?
   A: 그는 물리학자이자 수학자였습니다.
❹ Q: 중력이란 무엇인가요?
   A: 중력이란 태양 주변 궤도 안에서 행성이 돌게끔 유지하는 힘입니다.

| Step 4 | 교과서 받아쓰기 | p. 37 |

Isaac Newton and Thomas Edison

Isaac Newton (1643-1727) was a physicist and mathematician. He studied forces and light. He realized there must be a force that keeps the planets in orbit around the sun. Today, we know this force as gravity.

Thomas Edison (1847-1931) was an inventor. At 12, he suffered from scarlet fever and became deaf. However, he made more than 1,000 inventions, including long-lasting light bulbs and batteries.

＊지문 해석

아이작 뉴턴과 토머스 에디슨

아이작 뉴턴(1643-1727)은 물리학자이자 수학자였습니다. 그는 힘과 빛에 대해 연구했습니다. 그는 태양 주변 궤도 안에서 행성이 돌게끔 유지하는 힘이 존재한다는 것을 깨달았습니다. 오늘날, 우리는 이 힘을 중력이라고 알고 있죠.

토머스 에디슨(1847-1931)은 발명가였습니다. 12살 때, 그는 열병을 앓았고, 귀가 멀게 되었습니다. 그러나, 그는 오래 지속되는 전구와 건전지를 포함해 발명품 1,000여 가지를 만들었습니다.

Unit 06

Inventions

| Step 1 | 단어 받아쓰기 | p. 40 |

❶ use — 사용하다
❷ wheel — 바퀴
❸ create — 창조하다
❹ idea — 발상, 아이디어
❺ easier — 더 쉬운, 더 수월한
❻ magnetic compass — 자기 나침반
❼ character — 등장인물, 특성
❽ writer — 작가, 저자
❾ life — 생활, 삶
❿ invention — 발명품

1단계 느린 속도로 듣고 받아쓰기

❶ Paper was invented in China.
❷ Ideas can also be called inventions.
❸ Inventions have made life easier for us.
❹ New things that are made or created are called inventions.

2단계 정상 속도로 듣고 받아쓰기

❶ Inventions have made life easier for us.
❷ Paper was invented in China.
❸ Ideas can also be called inventions.
❹ New things that are made or created are called inventions.

| Step 3 | 대화문 받아쓰기 | p. 42 |

❶ Q : According to the story, what was the car when it was first made?
　A : It was an invention when it was first made.
❷ Q : What can writers invent?
　A : Writers can invent characters and then write stories about them.
❸ Q : What have the wheel and paper done for people?
　A : They have made life easier for people.
❹ Q : What do people call new things that are made or created?
　A : People call them inventions.

＊ 대화문 받아쓰기 해석

❶ Q : 이야기에 따르면 자동차가 처음 만들어졌을 때 그것은 무엇이었나요?
　A : 그것은 처음 만들어졌을 때 발명품이었습니다.
❷ Q : 작가는 무엇을 발명할 수 있나요?
　A : 작가는 등장인물을 고안하고 그들에 대한 이야기를 씁니다.
❸ Q : 바퀴나 종이는 사람들을 위해서 무엇을 했나요?
　A : 그것들은 사람들을 위해서 삶을 더 수월하게 만들어 주었습니다.

❹ Q : 사람들은 만들어지거나 창조된 새로운 것을 무엇이라고 부르나요?
　A : 사람들은 그것들을 발명품이라고 부릅니다.

| Step 4 | 교과서 받아쓰기 | p. 43 |

Inventions
New things that are made or created are called inventions. The computer and the car were inventions when they were first made.
Ideas can also be called inventions. Writers can invent characters and then write stories about them.
Inventions have made life easier for us. The wheel was first used in Mesopotamia. Paper was invented in China.

＊ 지문 해석

발명품
만들어지거나 창조된 새로운 것을 발명품이라고 부릅니다. 컴퓨터와 자동차도 처음 만들어졌을 때는 발명품이었죠.
발상도 또한 발명품으로 불릴 수 있습니다. 작가는 등장인물을 고안하고 그들에 대한 이야기를 씁니다.
발명품은 우리를 위해서 삶을 더 수월하게 만들어 주었습니다. 바퀴는 메소포타미아 지역에서 처음 사용되었습니다. 종이는 중국에서 발명되었습니다.

Unit 07

South America

| Step 1 | 단어 받아쓰기 | p. 46 |

❶ spine　　　척추, 등뼈
❷ flow　　　흐르다

7

③ south   남쪽
④ north   북쪽
⑤ run   이어지다, 달리다
⑥ east   동쪽
⑦ western   서쪽의
⑧ west   서쪽
⑨ side   쪽, 측, 측면
⑩ continent   대륙

Step 2   문장 받아쓰기   p. 47

1단계 느린 속도로 듣고 받아쓰기

① The Andes Mountains on the western side of the continent are the longest chain of mountains in the world.
② The fourth-largest continent is South America.
③ The Amazon River cuts the South American continent as it flows from west to east.
④ It is the second-longest river in the world after the Nile.

2단계 정상 속도로 듣고 받아쓰기

① The fourth-largest continent is South America.
② It is the second-longest river in the world after the Nile.
③ The Amazon River cuts the South American continent as it flows from west to east.
④ The Andes Mountains on the western side of the continent are the longest chain of mountains in the world.

Step 3   대화문 받아쓰기   p. 48

① Q : In this story, why does it say the Andes Mountains run like a spine?
   A : Because they run from north to south.
② Q : How does the Amazon River cut the South American continent?
   A : It flows from west to east.

③ Q : Where are the Andes Mountains?
   A : The Andes Mountains are on the side of South America.
④ Q : What is the longest river in the world?
   A : The Nile is the longest river in the world.

＊ 대화문 받아쓰기 해석

① Q : 이 이야기에서 안데스 산맥은 왜 척추 모양처럼 이어진다고 말하고 있나요?
   A : 그것들은 북쪽에서 남쪽으로 이어지기 때문입니다.
② Q : 아마존 강은 남아메리카 대륙을 어떻게 나누고 있나요?
   A : 그것은 서쪽에서 동쪽으로 흐르고 있습니다.
③ Q : 안데스 산맥은 어디에 있나요?
   A : 안데스 산맥은 남아메리카 대륙의 측면에 있습니다.
④ Q : 세계에서 가장 긴 강은 무엇인가요?
   A : 나일 강은 세계에서 가장 긴 강입니다.

Step 4   교과서 받아쓰기   p. 49

South America

The fourth-largest continent is South America. The Andes Mountains on the western side of the continent are the longest chain of mountains in the world. They run from north to south like a spine.
The Amazon River cuts the South American continent as it flows from west to east. It is the second-longest river in the world after the Nile.

＊ 지문 해석

남아메리카

네 번째로 큰 대륙은 남아메리카입니다. 그 대륙의 서쪽 면에 있는 안데스 산맥은 세계에서 가장 긴 산맥입니다. 그 산맥은 척추 모양처럼 북쪽에서 남쪽으로 이어집니다.
아마존 강은 서쪽에서 동쪽으로 흐르면서 남아메리카 대륙을 나눕니다. 그 강은 나일 강 다음으로 세계에서 두 번째로 긴 강입니다.

Antarctica

Step 1　단어 받아쓰기　p. 52

① cover　덮다
② desert　사막
③ average　평균; 평균의
④ permanently　영구적으로
⑤ consider　간주하다, 여기다
⑥ thick　두꺼운
⑦ South Pole　남극
⑧ windy　바람이 부는
⑨ research station　연구소
⑩ southernmost　최남단의

Step 2　문장 받아쓰기　p. 53

1단계　느린 속도로 듣고 받아쓰기

① About 98% of Antarctica is covered with ice.
② Antarctica is the earth's southernmost continent.
③ No humans permanently live in Antarctica.
④ It is considered a desert.

2단계　정상 속도로 듣고 받아쓰기

① No humans permanently live in Antarctica.
② It is considered a desert.
③ About 98% of Antarctica is covered with ice.
④ Antarctica is the earth's southernmost continent.

Step 3　대화문 받아쓰기　p. 54

① Q: How large is Antarctica?
　 A: It is the fifth-largest continent.
② Q: Can people permanently live in Antarctica?
　 A: No. No humans permanently live in Antarctica.
③ Q: How thick is the ice in Antarctica?
　 A: It is at least 1.6 kilometers thick.
④ Q: Is Antarctica a desert?
　 A: Yes. It is considered a desert.

＊ 대화문 받아쓰기 해석

① Q: 남극 대륙은 얼마나 큰가요?
　 A: 그것은 다섯 번째로 큰 대륙입니다.
② Q: 사람들은 남극 대륙에서 영구적으로 살 수 있나요?
　 A: 아니요. 남극 대륙에서는 사람이 영구적으로 살 수 없습니다.
③ Q: 남극 대륙에 있는 얼음은 얼마나 두껍습니까?
　 A: 그것은 최소 1.6킬로미터 정도로 두껍습니다.
④ Q: 남극 대륙은 사막인가요?
　 A: 네. 그곳은 사막으로 간주됩니다.

Step 4　교과서 받아쓰기　p. 55

Antarctica

Antarctica is the earth's southernmost continent. It is at the South Pole and is the fifth-largest continent.

About 98% of Antarctica is covered with ice. This ice is at least 1.6 kilometers thick. Antarctica, on average, is the coldest, driest, and windiest continent. It is considered a desert. No humans permanently live in Antarctica.

However, scientists live at research stations in Antarctica throughout the year.

＊ 지문 해석

남극

남극 대륙은 지구 최남단의 대륙입니다. 그곳은 남쪽 끝에 있으며 다섯 번째로 큰 대륙입니다.

남극의 약 98%는 얼음으로 뒤덮여 있습니다. 이 얼음은 최소 1.6킬로미터 정도로 두껍습니다. 남극은, 평균적으로, 가장 춥고, 가장 건조하며, 가장 바람이 많이 부는 대륙입니다. 그곳은 사막으로 간주됩니다. 남극에서는 사람이 영구적으로 살 수 없습니다.

그러나, 과학자들은 일 년 내내 남극의 연구소에서 살고 있습니다.

Unit 09

Australia

Step 1 단어 받아쓰기   p. 58

① except   ~를 제외하고
② island   섬, 제도
③ nation   국가, 나라
④ partly   부분적으로
⑤ part   지역, 부분
⑥ contact   접촉, 연락
⑦ contain   포함하다
⑧ develop   성장하다, 발달하다
⑨ far   멀리; 먼
⑩ without   ~ 없이

Step 2 문장 받아쓰기   p. 59

1단계 느린 속도로 듣고 받아쓰기

① It is the only continent that contains just one nation.
② The smallest continent is the island of Australia in the South Pacific.
③ Partly because so much of it is desert, Australia has the fewest people of all the continents except Antarctica.

④ Because Australia is far from all of the other continents, its animals developed without contact with animals from other parts of the world.

2단계 정상 속도로 듣고 받아쓰기

① Partly because so much of it is desert, Australia has the fewest people of all the continents except Antarctica.
② It is the only continent that contains just one nation.
③ Because Australia is far from all of the other continents, its animals developed without contact with animals from other parts of the world.
④ The smallest continent is the island of Australia in the South Pacific.

Step 3 대화문 받아쓰기   p. 60

① Q: How many nations are in Australia?
    A: Australia contains just one nation.
② Q: Are there a lot of rivers and mountains in Australia?
    A: No. So much of Australia is desert.
③ Q: How have animals in Australia developed?
    A: They have developed without contact with animals from other continents.
④ Q: What is the smallest continent?
    A: The smallest continent is the island of Australia.

✻ 대화문 받아쓰기 해석

① Q: 호주에는 얼마나 많은 국가가 있나요?
    A: 호주는 단 하나의 국가만 포함하고 있습니다.
② Q: 호주에는 강이나 산맥이 많이 있습니까?
    A: 아니요. 호주 대부분의 지역은 사막입니다.
③ Q: 호주에서 동물들은 어떻게 자랐나요?
    A: 그들은 다른 대륙의 동물들과 접촉이 없이 자랐습니다.
④ Q: 가장 작은 대륙은 무엇인가요?
    A: 가장 작은 대륙은 호주 섬입니다.

Australia

The smallest continent is the island of Australia in the South Pacific. It is the only continent that contains just one nation. Partly because so much of it is desert, Australia has the fewest people of all the continents except Antarctica.
Because Australia is far from all of the other continents, its animals developed without contact with animals from other parts of the world.

* 지문 해석

호주

가장 작은 대륙은 남태평양에 있는 호주 섬입니다. 그곳은 단 한 개의 국가만 포함하는 유일한 대륙입니다. 부분적으로는 호주 대부분의 지역이 사막이기 때문에, 호주는 남극 대륙을 제외한 모든 대륙 중에서 사람이 가장 적게 사는 지역입니다.
호주는 다른 대륙으로부터 멀리 떨어져 있기 때문에, 그곳의 동물들은 세계 다른 지역에 있는 동물들과의 어떠한 접촉도 없이 자랐습니다.

Unit 10

America's Past

Step 1	단어 받아쓰기	p. 64

❶	sail	항해하다
❷	however	그러나, 하지만
❸	native	원주민의
❹	early	초창기의; 일찍
❺	explorer	탐험가
❻	continent	대륙
❼	country	나라, 국가
❽	different	다른, 각각 다른
❾	later	나중에, 뒤에
❿	land	착륙하다, 도착하다

Step 2	문장 받아쓰기	p. 65

1단계 느린 속도로 듣고 받아쓰기

❶ But he landed in North America.
❷ While sailing, he thought he was going to the continent of Asia.
❸ Native Americans were the first people to live in America.
❹ However, many years later, explorers came to America from Europe.

2단계 정상 속도로 듣고 받아쓰기

❶ Native Americans were the first people to live in America.
❷ While sailing, he thought he was going to the continent of Asia.
❸ But he landed in North America.
❹ However, many years later, explorers came to America from Europe.

Step 3	대화문 받아쓰기	p. 66

❶ Q : Where did Columbus land?
  A : He landed in North America.
❷ Q : Where did Columbus sail from?
  A : He sailed from Spain.
❸ Q : Who were the Native Americans?
  A : They were the first people to live in America.
❹ Q : Where did explorers go to America from?
  A : Explorers came to America from Europe.

* 대화문 받아쓰기 해석

❶ Q : 콜럼버스는 어디에 도착했나요?
  A : 그는 북아메리카에 도착했습니다.
❷ Q : 콜럼버스는 어디에서 항해를 시작했나요?
  A : 그는 스페인에서 항해를 시작했습니다.

11

❸ Q: 아메리카 원주민은 누구였나요?

　A: 그들은 최초로 아메리카에 살았던 사람들입니다.

❹ Q: 탐험가들은 어디에서 아메리카로 건너왔나요?

　A: 탐험가들은 유럽에서 아메리카로 건너왔습니다.

| Step 4 | 교과서 받아쓰기 | p. 67 |

America's Past

Native Americans were the first people to live in America.

However, many years later, explorers came to America from Europe. One early explorer was Christopher Columbus.

Columbus sailed from Spain. While sailing, he thought he was going to the continent of Asia. But he landed in North America. He did not know that.

After Columbus, explorers from different countries went to America.

＊지문 해석

아메리카의 과거

아메리카 원주민은 최초로 아메리카에 살았던 사람들입니다.

하지만 많은 세월이 지난 뒤에, 탐험가들이 유럽에서 아메리카로 건너왔습니다. 크리스토퍼 콜럼버스는 초기 탐험가 중 한 사람이었습니다.

콜럼버스는 스페인에서 항해를 시작했습니다. 항해를 하면서, 그는 아시아 대륙으로 가고 있다고 생각했습니다. 하지만 그는 북아메리카에 도착했습니다. 그는 그 사실을 알지 못했죠.

콜럼버스 이후, 많은 나라의 탐험가들이 아메리카로 갔습니다.

Unit 11

The Pilgrims

| Step 1 | 단어 받아쓰기 | p. 70 |

❶	travel	이주하다, 여행하다
❷	Pilgrim	청교도, 순례자
❸	colony	식민지
❹	rule	다스리다, 통치하다
❺	build	짓다, 건설하다
❻	colonist	식민지 주민
❼	church	교회
❽	difference	차이, 다른 점
❾	group	집단, 그룹
❿	religious	종교적인

| Step 2 | 문장 받아쓰기 | p. 71 |

1단계 느린 속도로 듣고 받아쓰기

❶ A person who lives in a colony is called a colonist.

❷ The Pilgrims built a colony called Plymouth.

❸ A colony is a place ruled by another country.

❹ The Pilgrims left England because of religious differences with the Church of England.

2단계 정상 속도로 듣고 받아쓰기

❶ The Pilgrims built a colony called Plymouth.

❷ A person who lives in a colony is called a colonist.

❸ The Pilgrims left England because of religious differences with the Church of England.

❹ A colony is a place ruled by another country.

❶ Q : Why did the Pilgrims leave England?
   A : Because of religious differences with the Church of England.
❷ Q : What was the name of the ship that the Pilgrims traveled on?
   A : The name of the ship the Pilgrims traveled on was the *Mayflower*.
❸ Q : Which country ruled Plymouth?
   A : England ruled Plymouth.
❹ Q : What did the Pilgrims build as a colony?
   A : The Pilgrims built Plymouth as a colony.

＊ 대화문 받아쓰기 해석

❶ Q : 청교도들은 왜 영국을 떠났습니까?
   A : 영국 국교회와의 종교적인 차이 때문입니다.
❷ Q : 청교도들이 타고 이주한 배의 이름은 무엇이었습니까?
   A : 청교도들이 타고 이주한 배의 이름은 '메이플라워' 였습니다.
❸ Q : 플리머스는 어느 나라가 다스렸나요?
   A : 영국이 플리머스를 통치했습니다.
❹ Q : 청교도들은 식민지로 무엇을 세웠나요?
   A : 청교도들은 식민지로 플리머스를 세웠습니다.

Step 4 교과서 받아쓰기 p. 73

The Pilgrims
The Pilgrims were a group of people who traveled from England to America on a ship called the *Mayflower*. The Pilgrims left England because of religious differences with the Church of England. The Pilgrims built a colony called Plymouth. A colony is a place ruled by another country. Plymouth was ruled by England. A person who lives in a colony is called a colonist.

＊ 지문 해석

청교도
청교도는 '메이플라워'라고 불렸던 배를 타고 영국에서 미국으로 이주했던 사람들의 집단입니다. 청교도는 영국 국교회와의

종교적인 차이 때문에 영국을 떠났습니다.
청교도는 플리머스라고 불린 식민지를 세웠습니다. 식민지란, 다른 나라의 지배를 받는 곳이죠. 플리머스는 영국의 통치를 받았습니다. 식민지에 거주하는 사람을 식민지 주민이라고 부릅니다.

Unit 12

Slavery

Step 1 단어 받아쓰기 p. 76

❶ war   전쟁
❷ law   법, 법률
❸ force   강제로 ~하게 하다
❹ freedom   자유
❺ against   ~에 반대하는
❻ state   주(州)
❼ allow   허락하다
❽ pay   보수
❾ slavery   노예제도
❿ act   행위, 법률

Step 2 문장 받아쓰기 p. 77

1단계 느린 속도로 듣고 받아쓰기

❶ There was a war between them called the Civil War.
❷ In the United States of America, many states had laws that allowed slavery.
❸ Many people in the northern part of the country wanted laws against slavery.
❹ After the war ended in 1865, slavery became against the law.

❶ In the United States of America, many states had laws that allowed slavery.
❷ Many people in the northern part of the country wanted laws against slavery.
❸ There was a war between them called the Civil War.
❹ After the war ended in 1865, slavery became against the law.

Step 3　대화문 받아쓰기　p. 78

❶ Q : What is slavery?
   A : Slavery is the act of forcing people to work without pay and taking away their freedom.
❷ Q : What did people in the southern part of the United States want?
   A : They wanted to keep slavery.
❸ Q : What did people in the northern part of the United States want?
   A : They wanted laws against slavery.
❹ Q : What happened between the northern part and the southern part of the United States?
   A : The Civil War happened between them.

* 대화문 받아쓰기 해석

❶ Q : 노예제도란 무엇인가요?
   A : 노예제도란 보수도 없이 사람들로 하여금 강제로 일하게 하고 그들의 자유를 빼앗는 법률입니다.
❷ Q : 미국의 남부지역의 사람들은 무엇을 원했나요?
   A : 그들은 노예제도를 계속 유지하기를 원했습니다.
❸ Q : 미국의 북부지역의 사람들은 무엇을 원했나요?
   A : 그들은 노예제도에 반대하는 법을 원했습니다.
❹ Q : 미국의 북부지역과 남부지역 사이에 무슨 일이 일어났나요?
   A : 그들 사이에 남북전쟁이 일어났습니다.

Step 4　교과서 받아쓰기　p. 79

Slavery

In the United States of America, many states had laws that allowed slavery. Slavery is the act of forcing people to work without pay and taking away their freedom.
Many people in the northern part of the country wanted laws against slavery. Many people in the southern part wanted to keep slavery.
There was a war between them called the Civil War. After the war ended in 1865, slavery became against the law.

* 지문 해석

노예제도

미국에서는, 많은 주(州)가 노예제도를 허가하는 법을 가지고 있었습니다. 노예제도는 보수도 없이 사람들로 하여금 강제로 일하게 하고 그들의 자유를 빼앗는 법률입니다.
미국 북부지역의 많은 사람들은 노예제도에 반대하는 법을 원했습니다. 남부지역의 많은 사람들은 노예제도를 계속 유지하기를 원했습니다.
그들 사이에 남북전쟁으로 불리는 전쟁이 일어났습니다. 1865년에 그 전쟁이 끝난 뒤, 노예제도는 법을 위반하는 것이 되었습니다.

Unit 13

Melody and Rhythm

Step 1　단어 받아쓰기　p. 82

❶ melody　　　멜로디
❷ length　　　길이
❸ toe　　　발가락
❹ group　　　집합

⑤ note　　　　　　　음, 음표
⑥ rhythm　　　　　　리듬
⑦ tap　　　　　　　박자를 맞추다
⑧ clap　　　　　　　박수치다
⑨ instrument　　　　악기, 도구
⑩ play　　　　　　　연주하다

② Q : 당신이 드럼을 치거나 박수를 치는 것은 무엇입니까?
　　A : 그것은 리듬입니다.
③ Q : 여러분이 노래를 부를 때, 여러분이 노래하는 부분은 무엇입니까?
　　A : 그것은 멜로디입니다.
④ Q : 우리는 멜로디를 위해 악기로 무엇을 할 수 있습니까?
　　A : 우리는 악기로 멜로디를 연주할 수 있습니다.

Step 2　문장 받아쓰기　　　p. 83

1단계 느린 속도로 듣고 받아쓰기

① The rhythm is the length of the notes.
② When you sing a song, the part that you are singing is the melody.
③ It is a group of notes.
④ Melodies have rhythm.

2단계 정상 속도로 듣고 받아쓰기

① Melodies have rhythm.
② When you sing a song, the part that you are singing is the melody.
③ The rhythm is the length of the notes.
④ It is a group of notes.

Step 3　대화문 받아쓰기　　　p. 84

① Q : What is rhythm?
　A : It is the length of the notes.
② Q : What is it that you play on the drums or clap with your hands?
　A : It is rhythm.
③ Q : When you sing a song, what is the part that you are singing?
　A : It is the melody.
④ Q : What can we do with instruments for melodies?
　A : We can play melodies with instruments.

＊ 대화문 받아쓰기 해석

① Q : 리듬이란 무엇인가요?
　A : 그것은 음의 길이입니다.

Step 4　교과서 받아쓰기　　　p. 85

Melody and Rhythm

When you sing a song, the part that you are singing is the melody. It is a group of notes. Melodies can be played on instruments such as the piano or guitar.
Melodies have rhythm. The rhythm is the length of the notes. It is what you play on the drums, clap with your hands, or tap with your toes while a song is playing.

＊ 지문 해석

멜로디와 리듬

노래를 부를 때, 여러분이 노래하는 부분이 멜로디입니다. 그것은 여러 가지 음의 집합이지요. 멜로디는 피아노나 기타와 같은 악기로 연주할 수 있습니다.
멜로디에는 리듬이 있습니다. 리듬은 음의 길이입니다. 노래를 연주하는 동안 드럼을 치거나, 박수를 치거나, 발로 박자를 맞추는 것 등이 리듬에 해당합니다.

Unit 14

Enjoying Music

Step 1 단어 받아쓰기 p. 88

1. learn — 배우다
2. flute — 플루트
3. guitar — 기타
4. concert — 콘서트, 음악회
5. listen — 듣다
6. piano — 피아노
7. violin — 바이올린
8. even — 심지어, ~조차
9. enjoy — 즐기다
10. way — 방법, 길

Step 2 문장 받아쓰기 p. 89

1단계 느린 속도로 듣고 받아쓰기

1. People can enjoy music by listening to it.
2. People can learn to make music.
3. They can go to concerts or listen to music on CDs, computers, and even mobile phones.
4. People also can enjoy music by learning to play instruments such as the piano, guitar, violin, and flute.

2단계 정상 속도로 듣고 받아쓰기

1. They can go to concerts or listen to music on CDs, computers, and even mobile phones.
2. People can enjoy music by listening to it.
3. People also can enjoy music by learning to play instruments such as the piano, guitar, violin, and flute.
4. People can learn to make music.

Step 3 대화문 받아쓰기 p. 90

1. Q: Why do we go to concerts?
   A: We go to concerts to listen to music.
2. Q: What can we do by listening to music?
   A: We can enjoy music.
3. Q: What is it like to learn to make music?
   A: It is one way to enjoy music.
4. Q: What can we learn to play to enjoy music?
   A: We can learn to play instruments.

* 대화문 받아쓰기 해석

1. Q: 우리는 왜 콘서트에 가나요?
   A: 우리는 음악을 듣기 위해 콘서트에 갑니다.
2. Q: 우리는 음악을 들음으로 무엇을 할 수 있나요?
   A: 우리는 음악을 즐길 수 있습니다.
3. Q: 음악을 작곡하는 것을 배운다는 것은 무엇과 같은가요?
   A: 그것은 음악을 즐기는 하나의 방법입니다.
4. Q: 우리는 음악을 즐기기 위해 무엇을 연주하는 것을 배울 수 있나요?
   A: 우리는 악기를 연주하는 법을 배울 수 있습니다.

Step 4 교과서 받아쓰기 p. 91

Enjoying Music

People can enjoy music by listening to it. They can go to concerts or listen to music on CDs, computers, and even mobile phones.

People also can enjoy music by learning to play instruments such as the piano, guitar, violin, and flute.

People can learn to make music. Making music is not easy, but it is one way to enjoy music.

* 지문 해석

음악 감상

사람들은 음악을 들으며 그것을 즐길 수 있습니다. 그들은 콘서트에 가거나, CD, 컴퓨터, 심지어는 휴대전화로 음악을 들을 수 있지요.

사람들은 또한 피아노, 기타, 바이올린, 그리고 플루트와 같은 악기를 연주하는 법을 배우며 음악을 즐길 수도 있습니다. 사람들은 음악을 작곡하는 법을 배울 수 있습니다. 작곡은 쉽지 않지만, 음악을 즐기는 하나의 방법입니다.

Unit 15

Musical Instruments

Step 1 단어 받아쓰기   p. 94

1. shake   흔들다
2. percussion   타악기
3. crash   굉음, 요란한 소리
4. pluck   뜯다, 퉁기다
5. strum   치다, 퉁기다
6. bow   활
7. blow   (입으로) 불다
8. mallet   나무망치
9. string   줄, 현
10. include   포함하다

Step 2 문장 받아쓰기   p. 95

1단계 느린 속도로 듣고 받아쓰기

1. Instruments with strings are called stringed instruments.
2. You play them either by strumming or plucking them with your fingers or by playing them with a bow.
3. You play wind instruments by blowing air into them.
4. You shake percussion instruments or hit them with your hands, a stick, or a mallet.

2단계 정상 속도로 듣고 받아쓰기

1. You play wind instruments by blowing air into them.
2. Instruments with strings are called stringed instruments.

3. You play them either by strumming or plucking them with your fingers or by playing them with a bow.
4. You shake percussion instruments or hit them with your hands, a stick, or a mallet.

Step 3 대화문 받아쓰기   p. 96

1. Q : What do we use to play the violin?
   A : We use our fingers and a bow.
2. Q : How do we play percussion instruments?
   A : We play them by shaking or hitting them.
3. Q : What kind of instruments are the flute and clarinet?
   A : They are wind instruments.
4. Q : How do we play wind instruments?
   A : We play them by blowing air into them.

* 대화문 받아쓰기 해석

1. Q : 우리는 바이올린을 연주하기 위하여 무엇을 사용하나요?
   A : 우리는 손가락이나 활을 이용합니다.
2. Q : 우리는 타악기를 어떻게 연주하나요?
   A : 우리는 그것들을 흔들거나 쳐서 연주합니다.
3. Q : 플루트나 클라리넷은 어떤 종류의 악기입니까?
   A : 그것들은 관악기입니다.
4. Q : 우리는 관악기를 어떻게 연주하나요?
   A : 우리는 악기 속으로 공기를 불어 넣어 연주합니다.

Step 4 교과서 받아쓰기   p. 97

Musical Instruments

You shake percussion instruments or hit them with your hands, a stick, or a mallet. Percussion instruments include the drum, xylophone, tambourine, and cymbals. When you hit cymbals together, they make a sound like a loud crash. Instruments with strings are called stringed instruments. You play them either by strumming or plucking them with your fingers or by playing them with a bow. The guitar, violin, and cello are stringed instruments.

You play wind instruments by blowing air into them. Some wind instruments made of wood are called woodwinds. Others made of brass are called brass instruments. The flute, clarinet, and trumpet are wind instruments.

＊지문 해석

악기

여러분은 타악기를 흔들거나 손, 막대, 또는 나무망치로 타악기를 칩니다. 타악기에는 드럼과 실로폰, 탬버린, 그리고 심벌즈가 있습니다. 심벌즈를 함께 치면, 귀를 찢는 듯한 소리를 냅니다.

줄이 달린 악기는 현악기라고 부릅니다. 여러분은 손가락으로 줄을 치거나 퉁겨서, 또는 활을 이용해서 현악기를 연주합니다. 기타, 바이올린, 그리고 첼로가 현악기입니다.

관악기는 악기 속으로 공기를 불어넣어 연주합니다. 나무로 만들어진 관악기를 목관악기라고 합니다. 황동으로 만든 것은 금관악기라고 합니다. 플루트, 클라리넷 그리고 트럼펫이 관악기입니다.

Unit 16

Keyboard and Electronic Instruments

Step 1 단어 받아쓰기   p. 100

❶ keyboard	건반, 키보드
❷ electric	전기의
❸ mean	의미하다
❹ electricity	전기
❺ popular	인기 있는
❻ pick	피크
❼ electronic	전자의
❽ note	음, 음표
❾ nowadays	요즘
❿ organ	오르간

Step 2 문장 받아쓰기   p. 101

1단계 ▶ 느린 속도로 듣고 받아쓰기

❶ One person can play many notes at the same time on a keyboard instrument.

❷ Some musical instruments like the piano and organ use a keyboard.

❸ The electric guitar is one of the most popular of these.

❹ Musical instruments that use electricity are called electronic instruments.

2단계 ▶ 정상 속도로 듣고 받아쓰기

❶ Musical instruments that use electricity are called electronic instruments.

❷ The electric guitar is one of the most popular of these.

❸ Some musical instruments like the piano and organ use a keyboard.

❹ One person can play many notes at the same time on a keyboard instrument.

Step 3 대화문 받아쓰기   p. 102

❶ Q : Nowadays, when people talk about a keyboard, what are they talking about?

A : They are talking about an electronic keyboard.

❷ Q : What is a feature of a keyboard instrument?

A : One person can play many notes at the same time on it.

❸ Q : What do we call the piano and organ?

A : We call them keyboard instruments.

❹ Q : Is the electric guitar only played with a pick?

A : No. It also can be played with fingers.

＊대화문 받아쓰기 해석

❶ Q : 요즘, 사람들이 건반악기에 대해 이야기하면, 그들은 무엇에 대해 이야기하는 것인가요?

A : 그들은 전자 건반을 이야기하는 것입니다.

❷ Q : 건반악기의 특징은 무엇인가요?

A : 한 사람이 많은 음을 동시에 연주할 수 있습니다.

❸ Q : 우리는 피아노와 오르간을 무엇이라고 하나요?

A : 우리는 그것들을 건반악기라고 합니다.

❹ Q : 전기 기타는 피크로만 연주하나요?

A : 아니요. 그것은 손가락으로도 연주할 수 있습니다.

Step 4　교과서 받아쓰기　　p. 103

Keyboard and Electronic Instruments

Some musical instruments like the piano and organ use a keyboard. These are called keyboard instruments.

One person can play many notes at the same time on a keyboard instrument: you can play as many notes as you have fingers all at the same time.

The harpsichord is a very old kind of keyboard while electronic keyboard instruments are new ones. Nowadays, when people talk about a keyboard, they often mean an electronic keyboard.

Musical instruments that use electricity are called electronic instruments. The electric guitar is one of the most popular of these. It is a string instrument usually played with a pick and sometimes with fingers.

* 지문 해석

키보드와 전자악기

피아노와 오르간 같은 일부 악기는 건반을 사용합니다. 이러한 악기를 건반악기라고 합니다.

건반악기로는 한 사람이 많은 음을 동시에 연주할 수 있습니다: 당신은 손가락 개수만큼 많은 음을 동시에 연주할 수 있습니다.

전자 건반악기는 새로운 악기인 반면에, 하프시코드는 아주 오래된 건반악기입니다. 요즘, 사람들이 건반에 대해 이야기하면, 흔히 그들은 전자 건반을 뜻하는 것입니다.

전기를 이용하는 악기를 전자악기라고 합니다. 전기 기타는 이 중에서 가장 인기 있는 것 중의 하나입니다. 전기 기타는 주로 피크로 연주하거나 종종 손가락으로 연주하는 현악기입니다.

Unit 17

Tahitian Landscape

Step 1　단어 받아쓰기　　p. 106

❶ intention　　의도
❷ look　　보다
❸ warm　　따뜻한
❹ clear　　맑은, 깨끗한
❺ feel　　느끼다
❻ bright　　밝은
❼ landscape　　풍경
❽ find　　발견하다, 찾다
❾ point　　가리키다
❿ painting　　그림

Step 2　문장 받아쓰기　　p. 107

1단계　느린 속도로 듣고 받아쓰기

❶ Can you feel his intention?
❷ Red, yellow, and orange are warm colors.
❸ In Paul Gauguin's *Tahitian Landscape*, as you can see, Gauguin used warm colors.
❹ He wanted to make us feel the hot sun and see the bright and clear sky.

2단계　정상 속도로 듣고 받아쓰기

❶ In Paul Gauguin's *Tahitian Landscape*, as you can see, Gauguin used warm colors.
❷ Red, yellow, and orange are warm colors.
❸ He wanted to make us feel the hot sun and see the bright and clear sky.
❹ Can you feel his intention?

Step 3   대화문 받아쓰기   p. 108

❶ Q : What can we feel through Gauguin's use of warm colors?

   A : We can feel his intention.

❷ Q : In *Tahitian Landscape*, what colors did Gauguin use?

   A : Gauguin used warm colors.

❸ Q : What did Gauguin want us to feel by using warm colors?

   A : He wanted us to feel the hot sun.

❹ Q : What are warm colors?

   A : Red, yellow, and orange are warm colors.

* 대화문 받아쓰기 해석

❶ Q : 우리는 고갱의 따뜻한 색의 사용을 통해 무엇을 느낄 수 있나요?

   A : 우리는 그의 의도를 느낄 수 있습니다.

❷ Q : 〈타히티 섬의 풍경〉에서 고갱은 어떤 색을 썼나요?

   A : 고갱은 따뜻한 색을 썼습니다.

❸ Q : 고갱은 따뜻한 색을 사용함으로써 우리가 무엇을 느끼기를 원했나요?

   A : 그는 우리가 따뜻한 태양을 느끼기를 원했습니다.

❹ Q : 따뜻한 색은 무엇입니까?

   A : 빨간색, 노란색, 그리고 주황색이 따뜻한 색입니다.

Step 4   교과서 받아쓰기   p. 109

Tahitian Landscape

What do you feel from this picture?

In Paul Gauguin's *Tahitian Landscape*, as you can see, Gauguin used warm colors. Can you feel his intention? He wanted to make us feel the hot sun and see the bright and clear sky.

Red, yellow, and orange are warm colors. Now look at Gauguin's painting and point at all the warm colors you can find.

* 지문 해석

타히티 섬의 풍경

여러분은 이 그림을 보고 무엇을 느끼나요?

여러분이 보시다시피, 폴 고갱은 그의 그림 〈타히티 섬의 풍경〉에서 따뜻한 색을 사용했습니다. 여러분은 그의 의도가 느껴지나요? 그는 우리가 뜨거운 태양을 느끼고, 밝고 맑은 하늘을 볼 수 있기를 원했습니다.

빨간색, 노란색, 그리고 주황색은 따뜻한 색입니다. 지금 고갱의 그림을 보고, 여러분이 찾을 수 있는 따뜻한 색을 모두 가리켜 보세요.

Unit 18

Blue Atmosphere

Step 1   단어 받아쓰기   p. 112

❶ seem   보이다, ~인 것 같다
❷ painting   그림
❸ push   밀다
❹ artist   예술가, 화가
❺ cool   시원한
❻ deep   깊은, 짙은
❼ fiery   불타는 듯한, 불 같은
❽ atmosphere   분위기, 대기
❾ use   사용하다
❿ include   포함하다

Step 2   문장 받아쓰기   p. 113

1단계 느린 속도로 듣고 받아쓰기

❶ Helen Frankenthaler's *Blue Atmosphere* is a painting made up only of colors.

❷ Though the artist called this painting *Blue Atmosphere*, there is a lot of red in it.

❸ The fiery red seems to be pushing back the cool and deep blue.

❹ Some artists only use colors in their paintings without including people or things.

❶ The fiery red seems to be pushing back the cool and deep blue.

❷ Though the artist called this painting *Blue Atmosphere*, there is a lot of red in it.

❸ Helen Frankenthaler's *Blue Atmosphere* is a painting made up only of colors.

❹ Some artists only use colors in their paintings without including people or things.

---

❶ Q : What does *Blue Atmosphere* look like?
　A : It looks like the fiery red is pushing back the blue.

❷ Q : What can we notice in *Blue Atmosphere*?
　A : We can notice there is a lot of red in it.

❸ Q : What is *Blue Atmosphere* made up of?
　A : *Blue Atmosphere* is a painting made up only of colors.

❹ Q : Can we paint without including people or things?
　A : Yes. Some artists only use colors in their paintings.

---

* 대화문 받아쓰기 해석

❶ Q : 〈푸른 기운〉은 무엇처럼 보이나요?
　A : 그것은 불타는 듯한 빨간색이 파란색을 밀어내는 것처럼 보입니다.

❷ Q : 우리는 〈푸른 기운〉에서 무엇을 알 수 있습니까?
　A : 우리는 그것에 빨간색이 많이 있다는 것을 알 수 있습니다.

❸ Q : 〈푸른 기운〉은 무엇으로 구성되어 있습니까?
　A : 〈푸른 기운〉은 오직 색만으로 구성된 그림입니다.

❹ Q : 우리는 사람이나 사물을 포함하지 않고 그림을 그릴 수 있나요?
　A : 네. 어떤 화가는 자신의 그림에 오직 색만 사용합니다.

Blue Atmosphere

Some artists only use colors in their paintings without including people or things.
Helen Frankenthaler's *Blue Atmosphere* is a painting made up only of colors. Though the artist called this painting **Blue Atmosphere**, there is a lot of red in it. The fiery red seems to be pushing back the cool and deep blue. What name would you give this painting?

---

* 지문 해석

푸른 기운

어떤 화가는 자신의 그림에, 사람이나 사물을 포함하지 않고, 오직 색만 사용합니다.
헬렌 프랑켄탈러의 〈푸른 기운〉은 오직 색만으로 구성된 그림입니다. 화가는 이 그림을 〈푸른 기운〉이라고 불렀지만, 그 그림에는 빨간색이 많이 있습니다. 그 불타는 듯한 빨간색은 시원하고 짙은 파란색을 밀어내는 것처럼 보입니다. 당신은 이 그림에 어떤 이름을 붙여 보겠습니까?

Unit 19

Lines

❶ line　　　　선
❷ direction　　방향
❸ straight　　곧은, 죽 뻗은
❹ bend　　　구부리다, 구부러지다
❺ circle　　　원, 동그라미
❻ spiral　　　나선형의
❼ vertical　　수직의
❽ zigzag　　　지그재그형

⑨ horizontal   수평의

⑩ diagonal   대각선의, 사선의

1단계 느린 속도로 듣고 받아쓰기

① The lines that are leaning are called diagonal lines.

② The lines that bend a little are called curved lines.

③ They are straight lines, but they point in different directions.

④ Lines do not have to be just straight.

2단계 정상 속도로 듣고 받아쓰기

① Lines do not have to be just straight.

② They are straight lines, but they point in different directions.

③ The lines that bend a little are called curved lines.

④ The lines that are leaning are called diagonal lines.

① Q : When a line moves in many directions, what do we call it?

    A : We call it a zigzag.

② Q : What do we call the lines that bend a little?

    A : We call them curved lines.

③ Q : What are diagonal lines?

    A : The lines that are leaning are diagonal lines.

④ Q : How does the line of a circle bend?

    A : It bends all the way around.

* 대화문 받아쓰기 해석

① Q : 선이 많은 방향으로 움직일 때 우리는 그것을 무엇이라고 부르나요?

    A : 우리는 그것을 지그재그형이라고 부릅니다.

② Q : 우리는 약간 구부러져 있는 선을 무엇이라고 부르나요?

    A : 우리는 그것들을 곡선이라고 부릅니다.

③ Q : 대각선은 무엇인가요?

    A : 기울어져 있는 선은 대각선입니다.

④ Q : 원의 선은 어떻게 구부러져 있나요?

    A : 그것은 모든 방향으로 구부러져 있습니다.

Lines

Lines do not have to be just straight. They are straight lines, but they point in different directions. The lines that point up and down are called vertical lines. The lines that point side to side are horizontal lines. The lines that are leaning are called diagonal lines.

Look at the zigzag line. It is more lively or active compared to a horizontal line because it moves in more directions.

Here are some more lines. These lines are bent. The lines that bend a little are called curved lines. The line that bends all the way around is called a circle. The line that keeps curving inside itself is called a spiral.

* 지문 해석

선

선이 반드시 딱 일직선이어야 할 필요는 없습니다. 그것들은 직선이지만, 서로 다른 방향을 향합니다. 위와 아래로 향하는 선을 수직선이라고 부릅니다. 양 옆으로 향하는 선은 수평선입니다. 기울어져 있는 선은 대각선이라고 합니다.

지그재그 선을 보십시오. 이 선은 더 많은 방향으로 움직이기 때문에, 수평선보다 더 활기차고 역동적입니다.

여기에 더 많은 선이 몇 가지 있습니다. 이 선들은 구부러져 있죠. 약간 구부러져 있는 선을 곡선이라고 합니다. 모든 방향이 구부러진 선은 원이라고 부르죠. 안쪽을 향해 계속 구부러져 들어가는 선은 나선이라고 합니다.

Drawing with Lines

Step 1 단어 받아쓰기   p. 124

1. curved   곡선의, 구부러진
2. swan   백조
3. painting   그림
4. drawing   그림, 소묘
5. neck   목
6. graceful   우아한
7. inside   안으로; ~ 안에
8. curve   구부러지다
9. French   프랑스의, 프랑스인의
10. spiral   나선형의

Step 2 문장 받아쓰기   p. 125

1단계 느린 속도로 듣고 받아쓰기

1. Curved lines can seem graceful.
2. In the painting, called *Shell No.1*, do you see one type of line that stands out more than the others?
3. A spiral line is a line that keeps curving inside itself.
4. There is a picture made only from lines.

2단계 정상 속도로 듣고 받아쓰기

1. There is a picture made only from lines.
2. A spiral line is a line that keeps curving inside itself.
3. Curved lines can seem graceful.
4. In the painting, called *Shell No.1*, do you see one type of line that stands out more than the others?

Step 3 대화문 받아쓰기   p. 126

1. Q : What type of lines can you see from the neck of the swan?
   A : Curved lines.
2. Q : What did Matisse use in his picture, *The Swan*?
   A : He only used lines.
3. Q : What is a spiral line?
   A : A line that keeps curving inside itself is a spiral line.
4. Q : What line did O'Keeffe use in *Shell No.1*?
   A : She used a spiral line.

* 대화문 받아쓰기 해석

1. Q : 백조의 목에서 어떤 종류의 선을 볼 수 있나요?
   A : 곡선입니다.
2. Q : 마티즈는 그의 작품 〈백조〉에서 무엇을 사용했나요?
   A : 그는 선만을 사용했습니다.
3. Q : 나선은 무엇인가요?
   A : 계속 구부러져 들어가는 선이 나선입니다.
4. Q : 오키프는 〈제1의 껍데기〉에서 어떤 선을 사용했나요?
   A : 그녀는 나선을 사용했습니다.

Step 4 교과서 받아쓰기   p. 127

Drawing with Lines

There is a picture made only from lines. The drawing, called *The Swan*, is by French artist Henri Matisse. What type of lines does Matisse use for the neck of the swan? Curved lines can seem graceful. Look for some of the other curved lines in the drawing.

There is a painting by American artist Georgia O'Keeffe. Look for the drawing on the Internet. In the painting, called *Shell No.1*, do you see one type of line that stands out more than the others? Do you see the spiral lines? A spiral line is a line that keeps curving inside itself.

선으로 이루어진 그림

오로지 선으로만 구성된 그림이 있습니다. 〈백조〉라고 불리는 그림은 프랑스 화가 앙리 마티스의 작품입니다. 마티스는 백조의 목을 그리기 위해 어떤 종류의 선을 사용했나요? 곡선은 우아해 보일 수 있습니다. 그림에서 다른 곡선들을 더 찾아보세요. 미국의 화가 조지아 오키프의 그림이 있습니다. 인터넷에서 그림을 찾아보세요. 〈제1의 껍데기〉라는 그림에서, 다른 선보다 훨씬 더 두드러지는 유형의 선이 보이나요? 나선이 보이나요? 나선은 안으로 계속 구부러져 들어가는 선입니다.